C000225470

This book is due for return ... or before the last date shown below

HEAD'S TALES

GEORGE NICHOLLS

Hamilton & Co. (Publishers)
LONDON

Paperback ISBN 1 901668 20 7

Publisher

Hamilton & Co. (Publishers)
10 Stratton Street
Mayfair
London

George Nicholls is married with four grown-up sons.

He was born in Yorkshire and educated at Kirkby Lonsdale in Westmorland. Before entering the teaching profession he trained as a research chemist in the steel industry and served in the Royal Air Force. A graduate of London University, he moved from Deputy-Headmaster of an inner-city school to a succession of three Headships. "Head's Tales" was inspired by his work in these posts, supplemented by his experiences as a local magistrate.

Dedication

To Professor Brian Stevens, my old school friend from Kirkby Lonsdale, who, combined with the effect of red wine and a Mexican Gulf sunset, persuaded me to record these experiences.

To my wife, June, for her suggestions, her positive criticisms and, most of all, her encouragement and support.

Foreword

"The world is passing through troubled times. The young people of today think of nothing but themselves. They have no reverence for parents or old age. They talk as if they alone know everything, and what passes for wisdom with us is foolishness with them. As for girls, they are foolish and immodest in speech, behaviour and dress."

PETER THE HERMIT 1274

From time immemorial mankind has been concerned about the less than acceptable behaviour of the youth of the species. As we approach the end of the twentieth century, it is fashionable to attribute general misbehaviour to a relatively small number of deviants, who cause a disproportionate amount of disruption, thereby affecting the well-being of the majority. If successful in their wicked ways, they exacerbate the problem by tempting others to copy them.

The author has always considered this to be the case and the following is a light-hearted account of how he, in four different schools in the 1960s, 1970s and 1980s took positive steps to discourage misbehaviour by unusual and, at times, outrageous methods. In particular, he found that pre-emptive action at an early stage prevented mild discomforts from developing into massive disasters.

The events described in this book are based upon similar, but not exact, incidents in the author's everyday work. Likewise, although the characters are based upon the author's experience, they are not precise descriptions of persons living or dead.

Of course, successful headmastership demands a multitude and variety of skills over and above the ability to curtail misbehaviour. Thus, the incidents reflect but a small part of the author's work. Similarly, the wayward characters depicted represent only a tiny proportion of the thousands of well-behaved girls and boys whom he has been privileged to teach.

George Nicholls

CHAPTER 1

"GETTING THE JOB"
'Among those dark satanic mills'.

"For as long as I can remember, Ladies and Gentlemen, my burning ambition has been to be a detective and I must say that this inclination has stood me in very good stead throughout my teaching career."

I was responding to the opening question of my interview for the Headship of Lea Grange School, Lancashire by giving a brief run down of my career to date. My flippant reply caused a ripple of mirth among the members of the education committee assembled in the council chamber of the local town hall. I could have gone on to tell them just how obsessed I had always been with the science of detection: how I had read the complete set of Sherlock Holmes stories by the age of eleven; how my nick-name at school was C.I.D. Firestone; and how my forte for solving problems at an early stage was bound to ensure that I would be a most successful Headmaster.

As it was my first interview for a Head-teacher post and as I was not sure whether the laughter boded good or ill, I did not elaborate. I smiled with the committee and tried to look as if I eagerly awaited the next question.

At the time, I was deputy-head of a tough school in Yorkshire and it was with some apprehension that I had set out on that crisp April morning to cross from my native county to that of the red rose.

As my old car struggled to conquer the Pennines I had no time to wax lyrical about the dramatic scenery. The winter of 1963 had been harsh and the last remnants of snow, still clinging to the north facing sides of the highest peaks, were gilded by the slanting rays of the early morning sun. I remember wondering whether this augured well: was this to be my golden day?

I reminded myself that my prime purpose was to arrive at my destination in ample time to eat a light lunch and compose myself for the events of the afternoon. It was therefore with much relief and perhaps a little trepidation that I began my descent into the foreign territory of south-east Lancashire.

My historical studies had taught me that this region had been more involved in the industrial revolution than had any other part of Britain. Indeed, I had always felt that it was in the cotton industry where the most spectacular inventions of the eighteenth and nineteenth centuries had occurred. Yet I wondered if the landscape developments in the wake of Kay, Hargreaves, Arkwright and Crompton would present a less than desirable environment in which to raise my sons notwithstanding my wife's likely reactions. Would it be a land of cobbled streets, terrace houses, gas tanks and chimneys? I was to be pleasantly surprised to discover that the main industry of Lancashire was farming and therefore not dependent upon urban settlements, although I found the incidence of high chimneys rising from small factory buildings, dotted about an otherwise rural countryside, to be somehow incongruous.

So far, so good, and there was always the bonus upon which I could fall back: the fact that association football was flourishing in my target area. Burnley was still in its heyday in the upper part of Division One and two other teams, Blackburn Rovers and Bolton Wonderers, were also in the top flight. These were the days when teams only changed the colour of their kit if it clashed with an opponent's.

By the time, I had parked my car within walking distance of the town hall and taken refreshment, for which I had no appetite, I had decided that it would be tactically sound to report fifteen minutes early. My name was ticked off from a clipboard list in the foyer by a friendly gentleman dressed in black coat and vest, pinstriped trousers, and sporting a winged collar and half-moon spectacles. His broad Lancashire dialect welcomed me to Beckbridge.

"It's a gradely little place."

"Yes. I'm very impressed. Have you lived here all your life?"

"Not yet, Sir. I hope to enjoy a few more years before they cart me off to Fell-side grave-yard."

Surely, his old joke was designed to make me smile, to put me at ease. On the first count it succeeded: I don't know about the second.

He shook his head and chuckled. Then he asked me if I'd had a good journey, swung back the criss-cross gates of an ancient lift and I was dispatched to the top floor.

As I stepped out on to cork tiles, I was vaguely aware of polished wood, well-preserved leather, a maze of neatly arranged pot plants and low hanging crystal chandeliers. In front of me, placed where the most nervous of candidates could not fail to see it, stood an easel, which supported a board displaying an arrangement of magnetic letters. It pointed the way to the waiting room.

Two of my fellow candidates had already arrived and they were talking earnestly as I entered. One of them rose, introduced himself as John Jeffries and immediately invited me to call him "J.J." His genuine handshake and the warmth of his smile were most reassuring and by the time he turned to introduce me to his colleague I was feeling less apprehensive. The second man extended his hand to me without rising and my immediate impression was that, if he was suitably attired for the interview, then I was over-dressed. He was wearing heavy brown brogues, a mingled green and brown tweed suit and a round-necked fair-isle pullover, out of which peeped the knot of a dark blue tie. At no time did he smile and his imperious expression, Roman nose and bald head prompted me to liken him to Julius Caesar. Before I had time to decide whether the frivolity of allocating nick-names to my rivals would undermine the seriousness with which I should treat my first interview, two other candidates entered the waiting room: Hopalong Cassidy and Napoleon. Short exclamations of greeting were uttered:

"Hello J.J. You here again."

3

"How are you Eric? How's the leg mending?"

"Very well thanks, I'll be back on the mountains in a couple of months."

"I thought you were giving this one a miss!"

And so on. Obviously they were all well acquainted and when our host from the foyer came in to say that there would only be the five of us for interview as a Mr Hope had withdrawn, the reaction of my new friends confirmed my suspicions beyond doubt.

"Crafty sod. He's holding back for the new school in Accrington."

"No sir," said our mentor, lowering his voice to a confidential pitch he went on, "I shouldn't tell you this but I understand he accepted a Headship in Wolverhampton yesterday afternoon." He looked uncomfortable at the stunned silence that followed this disclosure. "I'll leave you then gentlemen. The committee and Mr Parsons are all here, so you won't be kept waiting long. Good luck!"

As soon as the door closed, everyone seemed to start talking at once, the gist of the matter being that Charlie Hope had worked a "fast one" on them by not informing them that he had been firing arrows out of their common territory; especially as far as the Midlands! I realised that I had infiltrated the South Lancashire circus of indomitable Headship applicants. I wondered how long I would be in the ring.

J.J. sensed that I was somewhat isolated. "Sorry about all that. We didn't get a chance to ask your name or where you are from."

I duly obliged them with the details, adding that this was my first call to interview. In response to this, there followed from them a mixture of advice and information, which clearly was designed to under-mine my confidence.

Caesar was Deputy-Head in a large comprehensive. He had been invited to apply for this Headship by the chief adviser to the committee, Mr Parsons, who wanted Lea Grange to be developed on similar lines to his present school, which had a reputation in the area second to none.

4

Hopalong had likewise been asked to consider taking the Head's post as Lea Grange had a long tradition of out-door pursuits and he was a nationally known mountaineer.

Napoleon advised me not to worry about the committee. The person who would make the decision would be Parsons. He would be seated on the right hand of the Chairman and he would ask all the important questions. He was a hard man to please. Napoleon knew this for certain because he partnered him at bridge on the third Thursday of every month.

J.J. smiled sardonically and wished me good luck.

Napoleon was first to be summoned. When called, he rose to his full height of about five feet six, drew in his ample stomach to enable him to fasten the middle button of his dark suit, pressed his palms to each side of his trousers, army style, composed himself for what seemed to be an eternity and suddenly paced forward to his execution. His short, fair hair, plastered down at each side of his parting, proved without doubt that brilliantine was still on sale in the area.

The drawing of lots had determined that I would be last but one into the arena and, as succeeding rivals went and returned, I noted two points of significance: the time scale for each interview was about thirty minutes; and those who had been in gave no hint, to those who waited, of the questions they had been asked. Trite conversation flowed freely and, whether it was a deliberate psychological ploy or not, by the time it was my turn to enter the chamber, my colleagues had convinced me that I could not hope to succeed at the first attempt. Perhaps this explains my frivolous reply when the Chairman had asked me to give the committee a brief synopsis of my career to date. If appointment was unlikely to follow one's first interview, I could at least enjoy myself.

Mr Parsons, who seemed to be the only person in the chamber who did not smile at my initial response, took over the questioning. After I had answered his first two thrusts, he remarked that I seemed to be obsessed with discipline.

"With respect, Sir," I observed, "perhaps you would be if you had my present job." I resisted the temptation to add, "and I had yours!"

"I have no further questions," was his sharp retort.

I had been in the room for no more than four minutes. Was this interview going to break the record for brevity? The Chairman cleared his throat. I shall never know whether or not he intended to dismiss me graciously because the voice of an elderly lady, firm and with clear resolution, announced that she wished to ask me a question.

I remember that I was seated on a swivel chair situated between the elevated bench, shared by the Chairman and Parsons, and the other occupied benches, which were arranged in a semi-circular fashion facing the Chairman. I slowly turned my seat so that I was fully facing my questioner. To answer her by talking over my shoulder, apart from being disparaging, would neither have demonstrated the importance I attributed to the question nor acknowledged the gratitude I felt towards my saviour. The ice broken, several other members of the committee put questions to me. I cared not that, with each one, Parsons seemed to become more and more impatient. In answering, I seized the opportunity to expound my philosophy: good personal relationships are fundamental to success in education; children, their parents and their teachers matter more than new fangled ideas; music, art and sport are invaluable to the atmosphere and the ethos of a school; children should not be labelled into categories of ability or they will perform accordingly and not realise their full potential. I concluded by extolling the value of praise and encouragement. All children have some ability and my task as Head would be to create the conditions and atmosphere to develop everyone's ability to the full.

"You were in a long time!" exclaimed Napoleon.

"What did he ask you?" enquired Hopalong. It was acceptable to discuss the content of each interview now that the last candidate had been called in.

"Very little," I said with resignation. "He only asked me two questions."

"You're kidding."

"No I'm not. He asked me how I would organise an assembly and then my views on uniform."

"But they're only the warm-up questions. What about your personal philosophy?" persisted Hoppy.

"Why were you in so long, then?" interjected Napoleon.

"The committee members asked me a few questions."

Caesar had been listening. He described my situation. "It doesn't sound very good son. You see, after J.J. comes out, Parsons will sum up for the committee and then give his recommendation. If you crossed him, you've no chance. Don't worry. None of us succeeded first time. That's how we came to know each other. Try again, but I should avoid Lancashire if you've upset Parsons. I believe Northamptonshire will be opening seven new schools this year." J.J. came out looking paler than when he entered. After we had whiled away about forty-five minutes in meaningless conversation, our elderly clerk entered.

"Sorry, gentlemen. The committee and Mr Parsons are at odds although we still hope to make an appointment today. The Chairman has ordered tea and sandwiches to be served to you."

Exactly one hour later the door opened again.

"Mr Firestone." I looked around at the crest-fallen faces of my colleagues. As I stumbled to my feet, J.J. reached forward, patted me on the shoulder and said, "Good lad!"

My re-entry into the council chamber is a vague memory. As I walked to the front, two or three councillors clapped and my elderly lady questioner whispered, "Well done, young man. I voted for you."

The Chairman formally offered me the post of Head of Lea Grange and I formally accepted it. "With the greatest of pleasure: I'll do my best," was all I could think of to say.

Mr Parsons shook my hand. "Welcome to the County. I'll be in to see you soon after you start in September. I've got to rush now."

I wondered if it was bridge night.

When I returned to claim my coat from the waiting room it was deserted. No doubt the little group would come together on future occasions. At least, I had done my best to keep the membership intact.

CHAPTER 2

"REALISING POTENTIAL"

'And unto one he gave five talents, to another two, and to another one; to every man according to his several ability.'

MATTHEW 25:15

At last, four months after my interview, I was sitting comfortably in the Head's study at Lea Grange School. My study!

Here I was, powerfully placed to expand my own ideas on education; ideas that had developed over the previous fourteen years. I knew that Adviser Parsons would be paying me an early visit, ostensibly to guide me but, in fact, to indoctrinate me with his personal philosophy. I looked forward to joining him in verbal combat so that I could expound my belief that good order and discipline are essential to any purposeful working environment. I was still smarting from his derisive attitude at my interview. Now I could demonstrate to him conclusively that the likelihood of prompt detection invariably deters would-be evil-doers and thus, in the school situation, prevents distractions from the fundamental purpose: the education of children.

Whether or not someone like Parsons, who had long-since escaped from the classroom, would understand the point I was making, was certainly open to doubt. Mercifully, my train of thought was abruptly interrupted with the realisation that the start of the new school year was almost upon me. Three days and seventeen hours remained. The Parsons problem would have to wait. I couldn't!

My mind had been made up long ago on the basic direction my ship would travel and on the fundamental philosophy that would guide it. All would be welcome aboard; none would be discarded; all would be encouraged to realise their full potential. My expectations of each pupil would be influenced and guided by the parable of the talents. The assessment of individual progress would take account of individual innate ability. All our children would be urged to give of their best but my staff and I would be ever mindful that some individuals find academic work easier than others. This would be of prime, if not exclusive, importance in measuring each separate individual's personal achievement.

The soundness and wisdom of this approach is best illustrated by examining the respective experiences of two quite different boys.

Peter was seventeen years of age, studying three A levels and submitting applications for university entrance. His father was a primary school head-teacher and his mother a solicitor. His splendid parents contrived to afford him wonderful support without over-reaching and thereby creating pressure. Subtle encouragement guided him into positive pursuits, notably music and sport. He was excellent at both.

Thus, it came as no surprise when he received an invitation to attend for interview at an Oxbridge college with a view to reading his chosen subject, mathematics. Deciding upon which discipline to follow at the A level stage had not been easy for Peter. The problem was not one of inadequacy nor shortfall: on the contrary, he excelled in the arts, the sciences and in foreign languages.

It is often said that there is a strong link between mathematics and music. This may or may not have influenced him. Whatever the reason, mathematics was his chosen subject and, two weeks later, he and I were caught up in the one-way traffic system, which plagues the ancient university town. A most courteous police officer directed us to our destination and ensured that we were only minutes late for our appointment. Would our tardiness signal lack of commitment and result in rejection? We need not have worried.

A most genial white-haired gentleman with pink cheeks and the hands of a surgeon welcomed us. The traffic was always difficult. We surely would be dying for a cup of coffee. We would be staying for lunch, of course.

When Peter and I were seated in comfortable, if worn, easy chairs our host selected a pipe from the four or five in his stand and proceeded to soil his immaculate hands by prodding tobacco flake into the bowl. From time to time he looked up from his task, peered at me over his rim-less spectacles, and made light conversation about the weather, about plants and shrubs, and about how weather conditions control the rate of growth of plants and shrubs. Peter was not included in our discussion. In retrospect, I think he was being allowed ten to fifteen minutes to settle down and adjust to what may be, for some, a formidable and intimidating situation.

Eventually, our host turned to Peter.

"I see you flew over to Boston with the English Lacrosse Team."

"Yes sir."

"Tell me about it. What do you think about the Americans? Lovely people, although they went bananas when Russia launched the Sputnik in 1959. You see, they realised that they were three years behind the Soviets. That's why they re-appraised their methods of teaching Maths, and that's how Modern Maths was born. Did you know that? Have you been taught the modern way?"

I coughed. "That's three questions for you to mull over Peter." I suggested. I had to stop the professor before Peter lost track of what he was required to respond to.

"Thank you, sir. I do tend to go on when I get started," our host smiled. "Your turn, young man."

It is sufficient to say that Peter did himself no harm by his replies. In particular, he was able to go into some detail about the inception and development of modern maths. As it was evident that our host was enthusiastic about the new approach, I felt that all was proceeding well.

Things got even better when our host opened the lid of his grand piano and invited Peter to join him on his wide piano stool.

"I've been wanting to try out this piano duet. I think it's Brahms' finest."

I was less concerned with the beauty of the music than with the fear that they would not finish together, which they did, of course.

"Splendid, well, that's enough for now I think. I'm going to ask one of my students to take you to lunch while I have a parley with your Headmaster."

Five minutes later, the professor and I stood at the south facing oriel window, sipping his best dry sherry. My host began:

"I won't keep you in suspense. Normally I would write to you but Peter has really impressed me. Providing that he gets two Es, I'll take him."

To refer back to the parable, Peter had used his talents to the full. He had "been faithful over a few things" so surely he would be made "ruler over many things." It is irrelevant that he changed his mind about Oxbridge and subsequently obtained a first class law degree at a red-brick university.

On the five point scale of talents referred to in the parable, Peter had been allocated the maximum. In contrast, Martin, our second example, just about merited one.

He joined Lea Grange at the age of eleven, moving from a primary school designated for handicapped children. Martin's difficulties first arose at the age of four when an attack of measles left him with partial brain damage. This affected his capacity to assimilate knowledge to such an extent that to describe him as a very slow learner would have been a monstrous under-statement. Yet socially, with his peers or with grown-ups, he was a delightfully charming young man.

It was this facility to exist and operate normally, apart from when he was required to produce school work, of course, that persuaded his parents to contrive his withdrawal from special education and, on his behalf, to seek entry to a mainstream school. They had reached this decision after very careful consideration and with the considerable advantage of professional knowledge and experience. Both were doctors: father was in general practice and mother was a consultant psychiatrist.

So Martin was admitted to Lea Grange on the first day of a school year, together with all the other boys and girls of the First Year intake. Naturally, his teachers and I were keen to see how he coped. Together with other backward pupils, he was given special help with reading and arithmetic: otherwise, he attended normal lessons with his class mates.

First impressions suggested that he had made a most promising beginning. He was popular with the other boys and girls and he tried hard to contribute in the oral parts of lessons. However, great problems arose as soon as he was required to write things down. On paper, his performances with either words or numbers were equally poor.

His parents were kept informed on a regular basis and they took what proved to be a wise and sensible view: Martin was happy at school, happier at home than he had ever been, and he was bound to make progress in due time. We must be patient.

He completed his first year with little academic progress to show for his efforts but one very encouraging development did occur. He won a place in the junior cross-country team and he represented his school in several races. Although his highest position was seventy-first out of one hundred and twenty, he obviously derived great pleasure and satisfaction and, indeed, pride from his achievement. After all, he was the school's sixth best junior runner out of a team of twelve so his place was secure and he could wallow in the resultant kudos.

Martin's pattern of academic achievement, or rather lack of it, continued through until the Easter of his second year. About that time something very significant occurred: he progressed from basic cross-country running to orienteering. This was undoubtedly the most positive development in his life so far in that, to succeed in orienteering, he had to read maps, measure distances and work out simple calculations.

13

During the early part of his third year, Martin's teachers noticed an all round improvement in his work. Some progress was evident in every subject but the advance he made in geography was phenomenal.

A second significant event then occurred in Martin's life and a decision was made which had as much influence on his future as did his introduction to orienteering.

His parents requested a joint appointment with Bernie Lord, Martin's Year Head, and me. After a few sheepish pleasantries, his father came to the point. They were both so delighted with his progress that they felt it was time for him to transfer to private education. They had been considering a move ever since his academic work began to pick up but what had finally decided them was that, the previous Saturday, several colleagues, with whom they had enjoyed a dinner-party, suggested that Martin should be in private education now that he was making progress. Unfortunately, Martin did not see eye to eye with them and, in fact, for the first time in his life, he was behaving badly: speaking rudely to them; refusing to come out of his room; slamming doors; refusing to help with chores, and so on.

I hope I did not reveal how astounded, dismayed and angry I was. Unusually for him, Bernie kept cool.

Father invited us to comment on the proposal and on ways of dealing with his son's tantrums. We talked at great length and gradually it emerged Father was the motivating force behind the idea and Mother had grave misgivings. When they eventually shook hands with us and departed it had been agreed that the move to private education would be put on hold. In the meantime, Martin would remain at Lea Grange and, if present indications were maintained, he would be entered for four C.S.E. subjects at the age of sixteen: geography and three others.

The next six years of Martin's education read like a fairy tale. He obtained four CSE Grade 1 passes. At seventeen, he passed geography "O" level. Two years later he achieved a Grade "B" pass in geography at "A" level together with a Grade "D" in Biology. He was accepted by a provincial university and he is now the proud possessor of a second class honours degree in geography.

"Well done, thou good and faithful servant!"

Somebody once wrote that comparisons are odious and, indeed, it would be wrong to attempt to compare the relative achievements of the two boys. What is important is that they had both used their respective amounts of talent to the full. It was not without relevance that they had been fortunate enough to be students at a school where good discipline ensured that learning could proceed with a minimum of disruption.

CHAPTER 3

"VERBAL COMBAT"

'The world is passing through troubled times. The young people of today think of nothing but themselves. They have no reverence for parents or old age. They talk as if they alone know everything, and what passes for wisdom with us is foolishness with them. As for girls, they are foolish and immodest in speech, behaviour and dress.'

The first four weeks of my headmastership had flown by. On a dismal, wet Wednesday afternoon County Adviser Parsons had "dropped in" to see how things were going. This was my first opportunity to clarify our respective positions on how a school should be run and I was determined to make the most of it although I sensed that the conditions were not in my favour. On the best of days, Parsons would be anything but amenable but on that day, suffering the effects of an unserviceable car heater and a severe head cold, he would be very difficult to win over. Sitting opposite my visitor, who gently dabbed his red-raw nostrils, I hoped that the warmth of my living fire would permeate Parson's bones and improve his humour. How was I going to convince this lanky, tweed-suited, chin-less expert that order and discipline were pre-requisites of any learning environment?

I finished reading out the quotation and went on, "One would imagine that these words had been written by a sour-faced, middle aged, commentator for one of today's more conservative publications. It's hard to believe it was written as long ago as 1274 by Peter the Hermit."

Parson's nasal problems were still giving him trouble. "A most interesting quotation, but I fail to see its relevance."

I remember wondering if Parsons had been bullied when he was a boy.

I persevered. "The point I am making is that the young always were, and always will be, criticised by their elders yet, essentially, they should be neither better nor worse than the children of any previous generation. If they seem worse, then obviously we must investigate the causes and do something about it."

Parsons cleared his throat and leaned forward to reply but I was eager to finish my point without being side-tracked. I continued briskly, "My theory is based on the premise that, in any group of people there are bound to be some non-conformists. This was so in Peter the Hermit's time and it's true of today. Take bullying, for example, I am sure that this is far more prevalent in many schools than people realise, let alone acknowledge, yet the effect on sufferers can be devastating. At the very best, academic progress is impaired and, in the most serious cases, some kids have even contemplated suicide. The secret is to detect trouble before it occurs and to prevent it from developing by coming down heavily on the perpetrators. I am not advocating brutal beatings; what I am suggesting is the creation and nurturing of an atmosphere, perhaps the 'in-word' is ethos, where the kids know that the Head is in control, where there is no doubt that misdeeds will be found out and, therefore, where study can proceed with the minimum of interruption. In such conditions everyone is happy. There's no need for any unpleasantness." At that moment two be-smocked girls from the Home Economics group contrived to deliver a pot of tea together with a sample of that afternoon's lessons: two iced buns, which were part of the teacher's demonstration. Our thanks and praise caused them to depart in the usual confused, blushing state.

Parsons returned immediately to the contest. With obvious disdain he said, "Mr Firestone are you not stating the obvious?"

"It may be obvious but it cannot be taken for granted. In the first place the theory depends upon the Heads' being in control. Some are not. I worked in such a school. The staff

17

suffered unnecessary stress through a combination of having to contain bad behaviour and being frustrated by not being able to teach. It goes without saying that the pupils' attainments were pitiful. I am determined that conditions at Lea Grange will be such that the teachers will be able to teach effectively and efficiently and the pupils will realise their potential to the full."

"Are you not being a little too melodramatic?" Was Parsons baiting me or did he really want an answer?

"Mr Parsons, I will be melodramatic. I shall describe to you what can happen in a school that is out of control. As an adviser, how would you deal with two boys who were armed respectively with a bayonet and a carving knife? Fortunately, they were about to attack each other, not me. It was potentially the most violent incident that I encountered in that school but it was by no means an isolated occurrence. The pertinent point is that the ethos of the school was so lacking that the two boys felt able to bring weapons on to the premises. Luckily, I had been in post about six weeks and had just about stamped my authority on the place, relatively speaking.

What is more, I was the Deputy Headmaster, and I could look back on twelve years' teaching experience. How could young entrants to the profession be expected to perform in such an environment? I had had to struggle to reach the tenuous position of authority which I had achieved. Certainly, there had been some improvement since my first day in office when, whilst I was remonstrating with a group of older boys in the school yard, a waste-paper bin, which was fixed to the wall behind me, suddenly burst into flames. Any delusions I had of dignity or control were shattered.

The school was situated in a deprived area where pigeon fancying and greyhound racing were prevalent. Parental interest was low: when a visit took place it was to complain about how their off-spring had been wrongly chided, often accompanied by the threat of violence towards the teacher in question, and hardly ever to enquire about educational progress. Such a school needed a firm hand: it was failing through the lack of one.

The chalk-boards fixed to the walls were always clean because every time it rained the roof leaked and water ran down the walls. 'Lead's been nicked from t' roof see, and t'education won't put it back no more.' A third-former had confided this to me on the first day it rained.

There were no doors on the boys' toilets. They had been spirited away one November 5th, two or three years earlier. Accepting Christmas presents from the pupils was a hazardous business: it was extremely likely that you would be guilty of handling stolen goods."

The glowing fire and the iced buns were having an effect: Parsons could not resist enquiring, "What was the Head like? What was he doing while all this was going on?"

"You may well ask," I replied. "I honestly cannot recall his ever providing any leadership or inspiration during the whole time I was there. In simple terms, he had given up. In these days of industrial psychology, he would be classified as, at best a bureaucrat and, at worst, a deserter. Rumour had it that, as a young Head, he had a very promising career in front of him but, owing to an aberration involving a member of the opposite sex, he lost the support of the powers that be. This became clearer to him every time he was passed over for promotions which he should have been rewarded with. Eventually, he lost interest in his work and withdrew into himself. The tragedy is that he was potentially very able and could have made a great success of his school. Instead, he rarely left his study, preferring to indulge himself with chain-smoking and studying horse-racing. His daily newspaper was invariably lying open at the page which listed runners and riders. I suspect that he placed bets via the school telephone because he regularly listened to racing commentaries on the radio system, which was controlled from his study. A most embarrassing incident occurred on the day that a horse called Santa Claus won the Derby. He had forgotten to isolate the radio system from the speakers that were installed in the classrooms and so all lessons were suddenly interrupted by an excited Irish voice describing the race's progress. Apparently, no doubt because of its name, Santa Claus had been heavily backed by many of the older pupils so you can image the mayhem when the race reached its closing stages."

Parsons shook his head. I thought he was about to smile, instead, he said, "Unbelievable. If there was so much chaos in the school, how come that he was not continually badgered by angry or even desperate staff?"

"Ah! that's when what he called his 'piece de resistance' became effective. Round about the time he 'dropped out' he appointed a new secretary: a highly intelligent and extremely smartly turned out lady who was approaching middle age with style and dignity. She wore high necked blouses under expensively tailored suits, always read quality newspapers and obviously had a standing arrangement with her hair-dresser. Her face was not unattractive but, coupled with her meticulous appearance, somehow contrived to be very forbidding. Only the most persistent of callers was successful in passing muster by her to gain access to her master. Through her ability to ward off trouble, to repel advances, she had earned her nick-name with distinction."

Parsons was incredulous, "But what happened when the fellow left the sanctuary of his study? Surely, he couldn't ignore what was happening around him."

"That's exactly how he did behave. It was as if he had an unwritten understanding with the pupils: he would not chastise them as long as they did not engage in violent conduct on the few occasions that he was to be seen about the school. It was most unsatisfactory. Whenever, he was unable to side-step trouble, he took the easiest way out. I'll give you an example. It happened during the year before I joined the school so I can't be sure of all the details. The incident concerned an art and craft teacher. The unfortunate man had a hearing problem requiring him to use an aid. His class management and control were deplorable and, in order to tolerate the noise, he used to switch off his hearing aid. Paradoxically, although it was the behaviour of his pupils that caused the chaos, these same pupils resented their own lack of opportunity to enjoy their art and to develop any skills they may have possessed in that direction. They did not accept that they were responsible for this: they blamed the art master and they despised him. One day after school, when the poor fellow was in the middle of the ten minute walk to his bus stop, a group of third year boys and girls pelted him with stones and laughed hilariously to see him cover what remained of his journey at a terrified gallop. The following evening, a much larger group of pupils lay in wait for him and the incident was potentially far more serious although, luckily, the fellow escaped injury. The next morning, he reported the matter to the Head. Whether, in his haste to flee, or whether he was in fear of even sterner reprisals, he was unable to name even one of his attackers."

"Surely it would have been fairly easy for the Head to identify them," Parsons offered.

"Exactly, and it would have been an excellent opportunity to build some control by making an example of them. 'There is a tide in the affairs of men and all that", I agreed. "But no, his solution was to take over the art class, every day, ten minutes before the close so that the master could enjoy a sporting start before the potential attackers were let loose. Needless to say, the miserable chap sought and obtained a transfer to a more civilised post."

"What about the rest of the staff? How did they cope?"

"Some coped better than others but they all had to spend too much time on keeping order and their teaching suffered. They all worked their socks off for very little reward. Naturally, morale was low and this must have affected their performance. The rate of turn-over was high and this, again, did not help."

"How did you manage to establish yourself?"

"By playing football, I suppose," I replied and I went on to explain, "I am an F.A. coach and within days of my arrival at the school I had organised a programme of coaching sessions at lunch-times and in the evenings. Most of the lads were football crazy and they were quickly won over. Furthermore, their behaviour improved generally, a development much appreciated by my colleagues, who joined in enthusiastically with organising regular lunch-time five-a-side matches. In fact, the staff formed their own team and received strong support especially from the girls. On wet days, we organised indoor games in the school hall, having negotiated the use of equipment owned by a youth club, which was based on the premises. In the days before these activities were organised, the school was completely deserted during the dinner break. The Head actually locked all the doors and the kids disappeared I know not where. I shudder to hazard a guess at what they got up to."

"He locked them out!" Parsons repeated. "He locked out his charges! You must be joking!"

"No, it's all true. I know I've been describing an extremely bad case but, perhaps because I've had personal experience of how bad things can be I'm determined to maintain control at Lea Grange. I shall lead from the front and create the kind of school that you and I would be pleased for our own children to attend."

"I can't argue with that. "All right, I'm almost convinced. I shall enjoy monitoring your progress. I must dash now, thanks for the tea." This time there was no doubt that Mr Parsons was smiling.

CHAPTER 4

"DETECTING MISDEEDS"

'Beware of false prophets, which come to you in sheep's clothing.'

MATTHEW 7:15

When I was appointed to the local Bench of Magistrates, one of the fundamental principles impressed upon me was that the accused must be considered innocent until proven guilty. In order to absorb this concept I had to perform a mental somersault because, in dealing with boys and girls, I had always believed that it is safer, and usually more accurate, to assume that the accused is guilty until proven innocent. Obviously, I hold this view, to some extent, with tongue in cheek, yet experience gained over a number of years has persuaded me that it has considerable merit.

Of course, when challenged about sub-standard behaviour, most girls and boys own up at once. A small number do not, their reactions varying between mild attempts to mislead and complete denial, even when they know they are guilty. In these few cases, I have always felt that, if overall control is to be maintained, it is imperative that the truth is discovered with minimum delay lest the temptation to deceive spreads.

I can recall three particular incidents that illustrate the lengths to which schoolboys will go to cover their misdeeds. The latter two are also good examples of how prompt detective work can bring instant rewards. In retrospect, all three incidents still make me laugh when I think about them.

The first case involved a twelve year old boy who, with his elder brother, was living in a children's home. They were victims of family problems and both had adopted me as a father substitute. Aziz, the younger one, small and undernourished, was particularly clinging. In the dining-hall, where staff and pupils sat at random, no sooner had I

23

settled down that he would pick up his plate and move from his seat to the chair opposite mine. As this happened on most days, we had long since exhausted topics of mutual interest but Aziz was never deterred.

One Monday lunch time he knocked at my door.

"Come in."

"Please sir, can I borrow thirty pence? I've forgotten my dinner money."

"Yes, all right. Let me have it back tomorrow."

The next day: "Knock, knock,"

"Please sir, may I borrow thirty pence?"

"Surely you haven't forgotten your money again!"

"Oh no sir, but I need thirty pence to buy some dinner."

"How come, if you haven't forgotten your money?"

"Well sir, you know I live at Waverley House?"

I nodded,

"And you know that I'm a Muslim?"

"Yes."

"Well, they packed me ham sandwiches for my dinner today."

"I'm sorry Aziz, I am not going to lend you any more money until you pay me back the thirty pence from yesterday. You must throw the ham away and eat the bread and butter. It will put you on until home-time."

"I can't sir."

"Why not?"

"It's ham paste, sir."

"Right Aziz, go to the kitchen and borrow a knife and plate. Bring them to me with your sandwiches and I will scrape off the ham paste. I will assure you that there is no ham left and you can eat the bread."

"I can't sir."

"Why not?"

"I've already eaten them sir!"

At my bidding, Aziz beat a hasty retreat with my words of admonition ringing in his ears. He was in no doubt that any repeat of similar conduct would destroy our mutual friendship. I controlled the urge to laugh until he had closed the door behind him.

The second incident did not initially strike me as funny but both Paul Robson, my deputy, and I have since laughed about it on many occasions. It began at about three o' clock one Tuesday afternoon and it concerned Paul who was on his way to a meeting. About a mile from the school and walking in the opposite direction he encountered Sydney, a fourteen year old. Paul stopped his car, wound down the window and asked Sydney to explain why he was out of school. As he received no reply and as he was already late for his meeting, he instructed Sydney to report to him on the following morning.

The boy failed to obey his request and Paul had to send for him. Needless to say, the teacher was staggered when Sydney told him that it was a case of mistaken identity and that on the previous afternoon he had been in school until the session ended at four o'clock. It was no accident that Paul Robson was a Deputy-Headmaster and no surprise that he eventually was appointed Head of a very prestigious school. He was a most competent professional, highly intelligent and extremely shrewd. Although of no more than medium height, he oozed vitality. He was a keen sportsman, an excellent musician; he had a great sense of humour and he was a tremendous supporter of staff and pupils alike. But try as he may, he could not persuade Sydney to tell the truth.

Eventually, he decided that, short of torturing him, he was not going to succeed and so he came to report the matter to me. I am sure that he did so with great reluctance because he was proud of his ability to handle his own problems and, indeed, any extra ones which colleagues passed on to him. In addition, he and I had an on-going friendly rivalry regarding our ability to ferret out trouble-makers and his ego was smarting. So he was very angry when he came to see me. He relayed the facts with clarity even though he continually interrupted the story to tell me how near he had come to laying his hands on Sydney, and even worse, it was clear to me that the result of Paul's interrogation would be that the boy would have taken up a firmly entrenched stance, which would be very difficult to shake. Past experience with Sydney confirmed that he found no difficulty in being economical with the truth. I am sure he regularly deceived himself.

When the boy stood before me, I invited him to relate the facts as he saw them. He was adamant that he had remained in school until four o'clock on the previous afternoon.

I purported to consult my desk diary then slowly raised my head and fixed Sydney with an even gaze.

"Then perhaps you can explain why your name was not ticked on the form register when we had the fire-drill at half-past three".

"Ah! That's because I didn't line up with the others, Sir. I had been feeling sick and teacher let me go to the toilet. After I'd been, I still felt sick so I went outside on to the cricket field. I was down at the bottom when you had the fire-drill."

"Tell me what happened at the fire-drill," I demanded.

Sydney described the procedure in great detail: how the classes walked out of school in an orderly fashion and lined up in their form groupings on the hard surface adjacent to the field; how registers were called to ensure that all those who had been marked present at afternoon roll call had safely evacuated the building; and, finally, how they all marched back into school. Only then did he rejoin his class.

Paul Robson and I looked at each other. His facial expression was indescribable but it clearly enquired, "See what I mean?"

I turned to Sydney, "What do you say when I tell you that we did not have a fire-drill yesterday?"

"Oh but you did, Sir. You've got your days mixed up!"

Paul could contain himself no longer. "Don't tell lies, boy. I can assure you that no fire-drill took place yesterday afternoon."

26

Sydney then committed verbal suicide, "Excuse me, Sir, but how would you know? You were passing the Spar shop in Portland Road at twenty past three."

So ultimately Sydney, through over-confidence, condemned himself by his own words. This is by no means the usual result in such cases of attempted deception. It is often necessary to probe more deeply to discover the truth and some people may question whether the time spent on such matters can be justified. The answer is irrefutable: schools which accept low standards quickly degenerate.

The third example of eliciting the truthfulness of a story again involved the splendid Deputy-headmaster. As in the case of Sydney, he was furious by his failure to disprove an explanation, which two boys were offering to cover their guilt. On this occasion, he was not alone in that others with far more experience and professional expertise were also deceived.

Again, the incident occurred during an afternoon. I had paid a visit to a local primary school and as I drove into my parking space I noticed a police van parked nearby. It would be the road safety demonstration team giving its annual lecture to the first year.

When I reached the waiting area outside my study a young boy sprang to his feet. "Good afternoon, Sir."

"Hello, Giles, are you waiting to see me?"

"No Sir, Mr Robson, he's in your office with some policemen."

In fact, six persons had laid siege to my private room, one, albeit, reluctantly. In addition to Paul Robson, there were two policemen in uniform, two plain-clothes detectives and little Rodney Thompson, whose blazer and trousers were covered in mud.

Paul immediately explained. "I hope you don't mind our using your study. Mine is too small to fit everyone in."

"What's going on?" was my predictable question.

"I'm Sergeant Fellows stationed in Beckbridge and these three policemen are my colleagues. This boy and his mate are wasting our time."

This boy was the diminutive twelve year old Rodney and his mate was Giles, the polite fourteen year old, who had just wished me a good afternoon. Could they really be wasting the time of this formidable quartet: two giants in the uniform of mobile policemen; a broad shouldered athletic specimen in mufti who clearly dedicated his life to body building, his own body, that is; and Sergeant Fellows, in plain clothes but unmistakably a police officer?

"How can that be?" I felt it was not an unreasonable question of the five adults who had taken over my study. I had hurried back from my visit to deal with several pressing matters. The last thing I wanted was to share my space and valuable time with these intruders. Paul looked at the sergeant. "Shall I explain?" he asked. The officer remained in his place, menacing Rodney with his towering presence.

"Be quick about it. I haven't all day to waste on this young man."

Paul explained that the two boys had reported to him how they had been set upon by three older boys as they walked through the copse on their way back to school that afternoon. Giles had managed to escape but poor Rodney had been bullied and finally thrown to the ground and rolled in the mud. Their main concern was that the attack had delayed their return to school, causing them to be late. They reminded Paul that they had been late the day before and that, on that occasion, he had warned them of the consequences of any future tardiness. Clearly, he would understand that they were blameless this time.

They were able to give him a useful description of their three assailants: very big boys wearing blazers identifying them with a well-known school a few miles away from Lea Grange. One boy had ginger hair and another had a plaster on his forehead.

With this excellent information in his possession, Paul had no hesitation in reporting the matter to the police, who immediately directed a patrol car to comb the local area in search of the attackers. When the officers reported a negative result, Paul contacted the suspects' school. He suddenly felt very uncomfortable when he was assured that there was nobody at that school who fitted either of the descriptions.

The possibility, nay probability, that Giles and Rodney had made up the story emerged with a vengeance. Paul and the two patrol offers proceeded to question the two boys but they stood firmly by their original account. It was then that, on the senior officer's insistence, Sergeant Fellows was co-opted. He had revealed his skill and experience immediately by arranging for the two boys to be interrogated separately, presumably in the hope that one's answers may vary from the other's. When I came upon the scene, he had completed a twenty minute session with Giles and he was warming up against Rodney.

"May I continue?" asked Sergeant Fellows.

I indicated my agreement with a resigned shrug and seated myself in a comfortable chair. He resumed his attack, employing far too many accusations and threats and far too few questions. The story was now clearly established, the boys had taken up entrenched positions and, without definite proof that they were lying, Sergeant Fellows was not going to force them to admit to anything. I allowed him a full ten minutes then enquired,

"May I have a few words with Rodney?"

"Carry on, Headmaster," said the sergeant, wearily sinking into a chair.

"Rodney," I said, "We aren't going to ask you any more questions so I want you to sit outside. I shall take you out to the waiting area myself. You must not say anything to Giles until I have asked him a few more questions."

I opened the door of my study and ushered Rodney out, carefully ensuring that I kept myself between him and Giles, who had stood up at our approach.

"Go into my study, Giles."

Having ensured that there was no communication between the two boys, I told Rodney to sit down. I then followed Giles, closing the door behind me.

I am sure that as he stood there before the four police officers and two teachers he was confident that he and Rodney had weathered the storm. What more could we ask?

I began, "Well Giles, now we know the truth about what you and Rodney have been up to, tell us which of you thought of the plan in the first place."

Giles' confidence visibly drained away. He jerked his head sideways towards the door and mumbled, "He did."

All four police officers stirred and my outstretched hand restrained Fellows from getting to his feet.

I continued, "Come on, Giles. You don't expect me to believe that. You are two years older than Rodney and more intelligent. You thought of the whole idea, didn't you?"

"No Sir, I swear that Rodney made it all up." Giles then went on to describe how they had realised that they would be late for afternoon school once again. Mr Robson had warned them only the day before that they would be really in trouble if they were late again. Rodney had suggested that they made up the story about the three big boys attacking them and, to add weight to the fib, he had asked Giles to roll him in the mud. They thought that Mr Robson would believe them and they didn't expect the police to be called in to help.

The two uniformed officers exchanged glances and smiled sardonically. The athletic specimen remained impassive, Sergeant Fellows was incandescent.

"You'll pay for this," was his opening sentence before he called for Rodney to be brought in. He then lambasted the two miserable boys until he could think of no further threats to use. Silence descended upon my study, broken only by the sobs of the two miscreants.

"Take them down to the medical room, please, Mr Robson, and bring them back when they have cleaned themselves up," I said.

The two patrol men were released by the sergeant. I turned to him. "You're not really going to charge them, are you?"

"I damn well am. They're a menace to society wasting police time like they did. It's time some mummies and daddies realised what villains their little darlings can be."

"If you do, it will be very embarrassing for both of us," I suggested.

"How do you make that out?"

"Well, in the first place, we should have dealt with the matter ourselves. There was no need to involve you."

"That's your problem. The fact is you did send for us." His uncooperative attitude brought a similar response from me.

"Sergeant, how will it look when you have to admit that, after almost an hour of grilling two small boys, you were unable to get them to own up? It only took me two minutes to kid them into telling the truth."

The sergeant's face contorted into a grimace. He was thinking deeply.

"All right, Headmaster." He paused. The sarcasm was unmistakable. "Have you a better idea?"

"Yes, let me deal with them. I'll send for their parents and I know they will co-operate to make sure that the boys are severely punished, especially if it saves them from getting a police record. In any case, I am sure they have learned their lesson."

The sergeant hardly concealed his relief and departed hastily, no doubt to grapple with more important matters befitting his rank and status!

CHAPTER 5

"RECALCITRANT FEMALES"

**"Matilda told such Dreadful Lies,
It made one Gasp and Stretch one's Eyes;
Her Aunt, who from her Earliest Youth,
Had kept a Strict Regard for Truth,
Attempted to Believe Matilda;
The effort very nearly killed her."**

HILAIRE BELLOC

Statistics gathered over many years demonstrate that girls between the ages of eleven and sixteen are far more motivated towards their studies than are their male counterparts. After the age of sixteen, the general trend is reversed and boys tend to catch up with and often outstrip the fairer sex. Whilst we all know what Benjamin Franklin thought of statistics, most people in the education of young people would agree with these general conclusions.

So whatever the reasons, and psychologists will proffer a multitude of them, the behaviour patterns of young males and young females do differ appreciably and there is no more powerful example of this than the difference in the way girls and boys respond when they are caught misbehaving. Of course, boys are more robust than girls and it is generally acknowledged that they tend to get up to mischief far more often than their sisters. The interesting point is to consider how the members of each sex react when they are found out.

It is inaccurate, even dangerous, to generalise yet the answer can be summed up very simply in the words often expressed by teachers, and particularly by lady teachers:

"Generally, boys tend to be more of a nuisance than girls but when they are caught misbehaving they usually own up. On the other hand, although girls transgress far less often, when they are discovered, it is very difficult to persuade them to confess. They are mistresses of concealment."

Thus, in examining instances of how school kids attempt to deceive their mentors, examples of boys are plentiful, usually humorous and invariably easy to detect. On the other hand, the incidence of misbehaviour among girls appears to be far less frequent but when it does occur it can be unbelievably wicked and the miscreants can be very difficult to discover.

Tilly was admitted to Lea Grange on her fifteenth birthday. She was accompanied by a doting, self-satisfied, if somewhat embarrassed, father who explained that she had just moved from her mother's home to live with him. He assured me that there was no acrimony between him and his ex-wife, from whom he had been divorced for three years.

Apparently Tilly's mother did not understand that a teenage girl needs her own space and freedom to develop her individual character. He informed me that times have changed: you can no longer insist that girls of Tilly's age must be in by eleven o'clock at weekends.

In fact, this was why Tilly had left her mother's place to move in with him. Apparently, every Sunday morning over the past few weeks, he had endured lengthy and often hysterical telephone calls blaming him for Tilly's failure to meet the eleven P.M. deadline. When he felt that he had suffered enough abuse, he negotiated the change in her home base, a decision to which her mother gave full support. Although the two homes were only sixteen miles apart, it was too far for her to travel to her old school and this was the reason why he wanted her to come to Lea Grange.

Finally, he assured me that there would be no problems for us: Tilly was very mature for her age. I did not bother to tell him that had been abundantly clear to me when she stepped into my study. She was tall, well-groomed and very good-looking but it was the way she moved across the room and manoeuvred her well-proportioned body into a chair that announced to all present that she was an attractive female and that she was well aware of it.

Father went on to tell me that she would be trusted with a house-key but, in any case, he was rarely late home from work. He was self-employed: he started early and finished early.

My colleague, Jean Lennox, and I surveyed our two visitors in silence whilst we digested the story so far. Something told me that life with Tilly would not be plain-sailing.

"That's a lovely watch, Tilly. Is it real gold?"

Jean had broken the silence.

"Yes, it is my present to her for her fifteenth birthday."

I wanted to tell him to let Tilly speak for herself.

"And that bracelet?"

I sat quietly and listened to Jean outline the basic standards of behaviour that would be expected of Tilly. It must have seemed to them that we were obsessed with correct dress and appearance but Tilly smiled demurely as her father continually nodded in agreement and murmured, "No problem."

In fact, Tilly became a big problem. Within two or three weeks of her joining us, Jean Lennox, who was responsible for girls' welfare, informed me that there had been a sudden increase in the number of girls reporting personal items stolen. Her initial reaction had been to instigate a thorough search of lockers and cloakrooms but recently the large number of incidents made this impracticable and she thought that I should be told. She was convinced that we had a thief in our midst.

There is nothing more demoralising for the members of a group than to feel insecure about their personal property: to be unable to leave items lying about in case they are stolen. People start to suspect each other and, generally, a pleasant, wholesome atmosphere can quickly degenerate. I was concerned particularly that several coats had disappeared from the girls' cloakroom. Understandably, we were receiving complaints from angry parents. One very valuable leather coat had gone missing and the owner's father was demanding action. A request for financial recompense would soon follow. Of course, the father agreed that his daughter should not have worn such a valuable coat to school but that was not the point. It had been purchased with walking holidays in mind and leather coats with detachable sleeves were very expensive, I was assured.

My instincts told me that immediate remedial action was required: the situation was bad but it could rapidly get worse. Unless we quickly exposed the culprit, morale would deteriorate, attitudes would change, and the habit of pilfering would be established. Step forward Detective Firestone.

Before I had time to instigate a serious inquiry, I was presented with a clue pointing to the thief. Unfortunately, my source was not completely reliable. A fourteen year old girl had been spotted wearing a new anorak, which had recently disappeared from the cloakroom. The sighting was bizarre, in that it occurred one evening outside the home of the owner, whose mother grabbed the girl in question, summarily recovered the anorak and notified me.

The following afternoon I was questioning the suspect in the presence of her embarrassed mother, one of the stalwarts of our Parents' Association. The girl, Penny, pathetic, gullible and none too bright, had been given the anorak by Tilly as a reward for keeping watch whilst Tilly took the leather jacket from the cloakroom. The poor mother was distraught. She pledged to do all she could to put matters right. She told me that she had already tried to recover the leather jacket. When Penny had told her the story the previous night she had telephoned Tilly's father. Unfortunately there was a problem. Tilly had lost the jacket.

All kinds of alarm bells were ringing in my head but I endeavoured to present a calm exterior. No leather jacket plus complete denial by Tilly, her word against Penny's, and Tilly would be off the hook. The stealing nightmare would continue.

"I think she took it for her boy-friend." Penny's welcome words interrupted my depressing train of thought. Calm and unhurried I enquired, "Her boy-friend?"

"Yes, Kevin." Penny was keen to rehabilitate herself.

"He's my boy-friend's mate. He's really nice."

Unfortunately, Penny was unable to tell me where Kevin lived but she readily supplied her own boy-friend's address.

Mother and daughter departed in sombre mood. I had informed them that I would deliver my judgement on the whole business only after I had interviewed Tilly and recovered the jacket.

There was still a long way to go and not a moment to spare. I knew that, within minutes of arriving home, Penny would be on the 'phone to Tilly, who in turn would notify her boy-friend. If he had the jacket, he would soon dispose of it and it would be gone forever.

I summoned Jean Lennox.

"How do you fancy a bit of detective work on the Eastern Estate?"

"I'd rather not. Isn't that where they are reputed to eat their young?"

I persevered. "Well I'm going and I'd like you to come with me. It's our chance to sort out the stealing once and for all. There's no time to argue. I'll tell you about it in the car."

The car was, in fact, a white saloon and as we sped towards our destination I wondered if it could be mistaken for a police vehicle. Perhaps that's why I raised my wallet to eye level as I addressed the man who answered my knock. I said, "We have reason to believe that your son, Peter, can assist us with information leading to the recovery of a stolen coat. We know he had nothing to do with the theft but we need his help."

The man in front of me was in his shirt sleeves. He had a frying pan in one hand, carefully balancing it to prevent the hot fat and sizzling sausages from spilling on to his door mat. He was wearing a flat cloth cap. He was clearly at a disadvantage.

"Pete, come here, the police want you."

Peter joined his father on the front step.

"We are looking for your friend, Kevin, and we need his address."

Peter was truculent and utterly unhelpful.

"Tell the coppers where he lives or you'll be in lumber. If you don't tell 'em, I shall."

After the initial euphoria of being mistaken for officers of the law and the advantage this would give us in our search for the jacket, I began to realise the problems we may be hatching for ourselves, let alone the danger of lingering too long in a hostile environment.

"Twenty-five Church Crescent." Father not son, gave the information.

"Thank you. Good day."

On our way back to the car I remember stopping to open my umbrella. Meanwhile, Jean turned. "The little devil, look, he's running across the gardens to warn his friend."

As we had no idea where Church Crescent was, far from being unhelpful, Peter's action was of great assistance. With Jean leaning out of the car window and issuing directions to me, I chicaned through the avenues of closely built houses and we reached number twenty-five Church Crescent just as our quarry was being admitted. I was soon waving my wallet on the doorstep in front of a well-groomed lady in a neat pinafore. I re-enacted my previous approach, requesting her son's aid without attributing any guilt to him. A shadow hovering behind her betrayed his presence so I continued my thrust:

"We know your son has the jacket and we know who gave it to him. We have no reason to believe that he knows it was stolen. We just want to get it back to its owner and that will be the end of the matter."

A youth of about twenty emerged. "What's up mum?"

"I think you know what's up, you were listening to what I told your mother. We want the jacket. If you don't give it back, you will be as guilty as Tilly."

"I didn't know it was stolen. I gave her ten quid for it. She's a class bird, lives in a posh house, her dad's rich. I never dreamed it wasn't hers."

"Why are you not at work, young man?" Jean was keen to join in the charade.

"I'm waiting to go in the navy, Miss."

"Forget it," she continued. "They don't let thieves in."

"I'm not a thief. I've got the coat. I'll get it."

To our surprise, he pushed past us and jogged to a hut at the bottom of the garden, returning just as quickly with the garment. He couldn't believe his luck that we had accepted his story. He wanted us to take the coat and go. There was no further mention of the ten pounds.

"Where are the sleeves?" The garment he handed to me was sleeveless but zips on the shoulders indicated the absence of detachable sleeves.

"There weren't any sleeves on it when she gave it to me" he assured us. I believed him, told him he had narrowly missed being charged with handling stolen goods, and we left.

By then, it was early evening but I resolved to complete my mission. I dropped Jean at school and drove to Tilly's father's house in the leafy suburbs.

"Mr Firestone, what a lovely surprise! Do come in, Father's in the lounge." Tilly was polite, hospitable, and composed.

"I've come to see you both, Tilly."

We were soon seated but only Tilly appeared comfortable. Her father and his secretary were clearly agitated. I suppose they were not in the habit of entertaining head-teachers to pre-dinner cocktails. I was not enjoying my work.

"I've come about a leather jacket that was stolen from school," I opened.

"Yes, I'm really sorry about it. We've spent all day looking for it in the woods. We got soaked and we still couldn't find it," responded Father.

It was true that it had rained incessantly that day but how was that connected with Kevin and the jacket? Why had they been searching the woods? Could it all be a big mistake?

There was much more to tell and he was determined that I should know how diligent they had been in their efforts to recover the jacket. He explained: after Penny's mother 'phoned the previous night, Tilly immediately admitted the theft and told him that she had hidden the jacket in the woods. As it was dark, they agreed that she would get it next morning and bring it back to school. Unfortunately, it had disappeared from the hiding place. Poor girl, she was so upset. He hoped she would be given credit for owning up so promptly. Anyway, he went on to tell me how he had contacted her social worker and how the three of them had combed the woods all day without success. The existence of a social worker attached to the family was news to me, rather ominous, I thought, but I let it pass. Instead, I delivered my bombshell.

"I'm afraid that you have been wasting your time. The jacket is in the boot of my car. I just need the sleeves."

Tilly's father sat open-mouthed. He needed time to adjust to this new turn of events.

"I think you should tell your father the whole truth, Tilly," I said. "I've been talking to Kevin so we don't want any more lies." Her father was puce, having difficulty in controlling himself. Tilly treated us to a plausible story. Kevin had said that he would like a leather jacket. She liked Kevin and wanted him to like her. She saw an opportunity to acquire a leather jacket and she seized it, literally!

"Go to your room. You're in tonight, young lady. I'll deal with you later," growled Father.

I saw my chance to clear up the mystery of all the recent thefts.

"Just a moment, Tilly, what about the anoraks?"

"Which one?"

"All of them."

She returned with five anoraks draped over her arm.

39

"Is there anything else?" I enquired.

"No Sir, that's everything."

"Haven't you forgotten the umbrellas?" I was guessing.

"Oh yes, sorry."

With Tilly banished to her room and the stolen goods at my feet, Father spoke.

"Mr Firestone, will you bear with us a little longer, I'm desperate."

I signified my assent by telling him I would now accept the drink I had declined when I first arrived. I needed it. Father obliged and then proceeded to recount a further astonishing episode in Tilly's young life. Apparently, the story he had told me when he first brought Tilly to our school was not completely accurate. The truth was that she had been living with him for over three months and her change of school had been enforced by her previous Headteacher.

The problem started one Thursday afternoon. Tilly 'phoned him at work. She was so excited. Her teacher had chosen her to fill an unexpected vacancy on a week's coach trip to France. The school required an immediate yes or no. The cost was £190 plus spending money. In view of the short notice, payment had to be in cash. Father was only too pleased to encourage her to take part in school activities and, next morning, a very happy girl with suitcase set out to join the coach for France.

The same afternoon, fate played Tilly a cruel blow. As father was finishing a late lunch snack in his office the two o'clock local radio news bulletin informed him that the coach taking a group of girls from Tilly's school had been delayed and would now be leaving at 3 o'clock instead of the arranged time of 9 A.M. He was almost ready to pack up for the weekend so he decided to leave work a little earlier than usual and surprise Tilly by calling in at school to wave her goodbye.

I had already worked out the ending to the saga but I let him tell me. Tilly was not on the coach. There had not been a late vacancy. The supervising staff were as puzzled as he was. Of course, Father had stormed into school and demanded an explanation: where was his £190 plus £30 spending money? The explanation was simple. Tilly had arranged to stay with her mother for a week on the pretext that he was going away on business. As her parents had not been in touch for over three months she gambled that her subterfuge would not be discovered. Getting him to pay the money was easy.

The Headmistress had declared that Tilly was no longer welcome in her school. The episode was only one of a long series of misdemeanours. Father did not wish her to stay where she was not wanted: I knew the rest of the story only too well.

"Whatever will become of her?" he asked no-one in particular. "I suppose you will be reporting the theft to the police?"

He was ahead of me and whilst I was still considering my answer, he continued, "I wish I'd listened to my sister. She teaches in Scotland in a convent boarding school for girls. She's been begging me to send Tilly there. The nuns are lovely people and my sister is sure that they would do wonders for her. It would get her away from the bad company she is keeping."

"I hate to see anyone as young as Tilly with a criminal record," I began, "but I am in no doubt that a drastic remedy is required. If you are sure they'll take her, I'll not stand in the way." I didn't take him up about who was bad company for whom.

"Oh they will! I know they will. She must be cured of her habit of lying. One day, she will cry out for help and nobody will believe that she is telling the truth!"

Poor Matilda:

"For every time she shouted 'Fire!'
They only answered 'Little Liar!'"

CHAPTER 6

"THE NATURE BOY"

**"Where the pools are bright and deep,
Where the grey trout lies asleep,
Up the valley and o'er the lea,
That's the way for Billy and me."**

JAMES HOGG

Expert powers of detection were rarely required to uncover Billy Gregory's misdeeds. His deviant behaviour was open, continuous and unashamed. In police parlance he required constant surveillance; that is if he, and potential imitators, were to be kept in check.

He soon came to my notice but our first serious rift occurred on the last day before the Whitsuntide Break, when I had been in office for almost a year. Several boys were absent on that morning and a long-serving member of staff explained: "The lads from the fells always break up a day early." Billy was among those who had unilaterally granted themselves a day's extension to their holiday.

This was just the kind of situation where someone like him could be dangerous: if he and his close cronies could get away with it, others would be bound to follow suit. I decided to take immediate remedial action. The monthly bureaucratic returns awaiting my attention were placed on hold as I set out into the hills in my trusty motor, armed with a list of addresses and a rough sketch map.

It so happened that Billy's house was my first port of call. It was one of four terraced cottages standing about 800 feet above sea level with no other dwellings in sight. The front doors opened on to the narrow neglected track which my map extravagantly claimed as a "B" road. I was unable to obtain an answer after several attempts so I decided to enquire round the back.

As I turned the corner of the building, my first impressions of the drab, forbidding row of stone cottages were completely reversed. I passed under a rustic arch which was adorned with a combination of Clematis Montana in full bloom and climbing roses about to flower. My path led to a surprisingly long, well-tended garden at the far end of which, on a patch of grass, a young woman was romping with a magnificent golden retriever. The dog was first to recognise the presence of a stranger but his bark was immediately checked by a crisp command and an affectionate stroke of the head from his mistress, who looked enquiringly in my direction. I ventured a little closer and, as our eyes met, I don't know who was the more shocked.

The colour drained from her cheeks. "Adam Firestone! You!" Then, "something's happened to Billy!" It was more of a statement than a question. I was confused, disorientated. "No Susan." Gregory was not this girl's family name when I had known her in our native village over twenty years ago. I continued, "What are you doing here?" I placed full stress on the personal pronoun.

"I live here. Billy's my son. What's happened to him?" With each word her voice became more anxious.

"Now don't get upset, Susan. Nothing's happened to him as far as I know. It's just that I think he's playing truant. Look, we're both a bit shaken. Can we sit somewhere and have a chat?"

Susan was about eight years my junior. Her brother had been one of my teenage buddies and she was always tagging on to us when we went down the beck tickling trout and stabbing snigs. I last recalled seeing her when she was about ten, decked up for a May-Day carnival yet, although her bright ginger hair had given way to a much lighter hue, she didn't look much different.

We spent the next half hour seated on two wooden chairs, which I helped Susan to lift out of the kitchen on to a small patio of natural stone outside the back door. She gave me a synopsis of the past twenty years of her life whilst Humphrey, the retriever, settled himself comfortably across my left foot. Susan had agreed to marry Jacob Gregory

43

when she realised she was pregnant. I refrained from asking her how she had managed to get involved with such a rogue. She went on to describe how, initially, the future had seemed so promising. Jacob had graduated in engineering and had no difficulty in obtaining a well-paid job in Keighley. Unfortunately his obsession with gambling had led him into serious trouble and they had moved house three times. Finally, two years ago, in an attempt to shake off his creditors once and for all, they had quietly moved and settled in this deserted area of Lancashire and Jacob had taken a mining job in Ghana. Clearly Billy was suffering from the lack of a father's firm control. Meanwhile, I was suffering from a cramped left foot as I persuaded Humphrey to move over to my right side.

"Ghana!" I exclaimed. "And you on your own with Billy. Why have you not been in touch with me before now?"

"I didn't want to take advantage of our previous acquaintance. When I read of your appointment to Lea Grange, I nearly did. How I wish I had."

"Well, that's in the past. Let's see what we can do about Billy and his future. Have you any idea where he may be?" It was important for me to locate him and convey him back to school both for his own good and also so that he and his peers would realise that I would not tolerate truancy.

"Oh yes, he'll be up at Brownlea Farm. His best friend's father owns it and when David's home from boarding school, Bill practically lives there."

In answer to my request for directions, Susan offered to take me by the short cut across the fields. Relieved of her pinafore and with her hair hastily tied back, she was soon shepherding me over the stile and along the hedgerow. A down at mouth golden retriever was left behind in the kitchen. We could not risk our expedition being compromised by a frisky young Humphrey. As we tramped along, side by side, my jacket slung over my left shoulder with my thumb through the hanging loop, I was transported back twenty years. Susan no longer had pigtails and, twenty years ago, little Sue would have trailed about ten yards behind the gang, near enough for her own peace of mind and security but far enough away to avoid being told to clear off and play with kids her own age.

Before Brownlea Farm came into view, I had learned quite a lot about Billy. He was a great help to his mother. It was he who had planted and cultivated the neat rows of vegetables in the back garden. He loved everything about the countryside: it was his natural habitat. He spent almost all his life out of doors. The only books he read were about animals, birds and country life. The walls of his bedroom were covered with pictures of British flora and fauna: some of them his own work in graphite, pastel and even water-colour. Recently, he had asked Susan to listen to some verses he had written. I was pondering on how different this picture of Billy was from the tearaway we knew when my companion informed me in a hushed voice, "The farm is just over the brow. We'd better move quietly now or, if they hear us coming they'll disappear through the back door and we'll never find them."

Neither of us spoke again before we were rattling the door knocker. We had executed our final approach across the grass, avoiding the path of noisy gravel chippings and so when David opened the door the two lads had received almost no notice of our approach. I say the two lads because Billy was clearly visible to us, attempting to conceal himself behind a huge oak door. Unfortunately for him, the hinges were specially designed to support the heavy weight and, as the stout door opened, a gap appeared between it and the jamb.

Whilst David was busy insisting that he had not seen anything of Billy since the previous evening, I leaned against the studded oak door, gradually pressing it back against the wall and effectively squashing the hapless Billy. By the time we had received David's repeated assurances that he would do all in his power to assist us, the prisoner had reached breaking point and his surrender was announced by a loud expletive. Lunch-time saw him and most of the other premature holiday-makers back in school, duly admonished and looking extremely foolish in front of their peers.

During the Whitsuntide Break, I visited the Gregory household on a couple of occasions and, by the time the school reopened, remarkable progress in the rehabilitation of Billy Gregory was clearly evident. Several events supported this belief but two were of particular importance.

The first indication of progress was his unsolicited offer to read me some of his poetry. "The words come to me at all times, day or night, but mainly when I'm in the open air away from everybody. Farmers and game-keepers would make great poets if only they could write it down. You should hear Tom; he's Dave's dad's labourer; talk about stoats and weasels and such things, yet he can hardly read or write." He went on "I'll tell you a secret. I get the rhythm of my lines by copying other poets. 'The curfew tolls the knell of parting day. The lowing herd winds slowly o'er the lea.' The rhythm is short, long, short, long, short, long and so on."

"It's called metre: iambic in this case," I offered.

"You're what?" he enquired.

"No, iambic is the description of that particular rhythm. It's a poetic term. Don't worry about it. You're doing wonderfully well."

"Thanks, Sir." He went on, "Some poems have a different rhythm. 'Spring the sweet spring, it's the year's present king' or something like that. I use the rhythm, that suits my feelings best."

I urged myself not to get too excited. We might have a budding Browning or a teenage Tennyson but let's take it step by step. In fact, we took a considerable leap when he suggested compiling a Lea Grange anthology of pupils' writing. He convened a small editorial group from the older students and the finished article, 'The Rainbow' because it was printed on pages of various colours, included blank verse, short stories and, of course, a selection of Billy's poems.

The second milestone, which indicated a change in Billy's attitude, was centred around a school visit to our native village in Yorkshire. As part of an 'enrichment' day when various group activities were arranged such as visits to cotton mills or museums, Billy suggested an adventure day in the Dales with an itinerary planned personally by him. I appointed myself as staff member responsible and we had a wonderful time.

We showed each other our favourite haunts, albeit separated by over twenty years. He knew the preferred nesting places of thrushes and blackbirds and he pointed out the meadows where peewits scratched their holes to lay their eggs. He skipped back and forth across the fast-flowing beck, using a combination of unlikely stepping stones and unbelievable skill and balance. I related my experiences in the Boy Scouts in the early days of the Second World War. France, Norway and the low countries had fallen and there was a real danger that Britain would be invaded. The Local Defence Volunteers, later called the Home Guard, had been mobilised and we Boy Scouts helped wherever we were allowed. I took Billy up to Ribble Head viaduct where we used to camp in camouflaged tents and watch out for characters taking photographs or acting suspiciously in any way. 'Fifth columnists' and collaborators had assisted in the fall of our European allies and we were determined that such traitors would not succeed in our part of the country. At the end of our watch we used to mount our bikes and furiously pedal the seven miles downhill to our village, then up the long drive to the rambling ivy-clad vicarage to notify the Home Guard captain that the Ribble Head viaduct was still standing and in safe hands. In true Dad's Army style, the splendid captain was also the village scoutmaster and the local parson.

When the day ended, a very tired Billy, together with a bus load of fellow pupils, returned to their parents. Susan, like me, must have thought life was becoming too good to be true.

Indeed, within a very short time we were jolted out of our self-satisfied, nay, complacent state. Billy was involved in an accident which was likely to result in the loss of his right eye. I received a garbled account from a distraught mother. Apparently David had fired Billy's shot gun accidentally and somehow Billy had been hit in the eye.

I went to the hospital as soon as he was allowed visitors. He resembled a First World War casualty with his freckled face and ginger hair completely hidden by a mountain of bandages through which peeped his sound eye.

"It wasn't Dave's fault. We were 'sat' by the fire with my shot-gun propped up between our chairs. Dave picked it up, put it to his shoulder, pointed it at the fire-place and said 'Bang'. I thought he knew it was loaded; just one cartridge that I'd been saving for a 'maggie' (magpie) that's been bothering the blackbirds and stopping them nesting. Then he must have squeezed the trigger because suddenly there was a real bang and the fireplace shattered. A piece must have hit me in the eye."

I tried to be as reassuring as I could, under the circumstances. Inevitably, our conversation centred on rural life and we progressed to discussing careers related to the countryside. We talked about possible entry to agricultural college: I knew well the one at Reaseheath and there was also another good one near York. Obviously now he had perked up, the nurses were sympathetic regarding the end of visiting hours and, when we parted, our spirits were much higher.

A combination of luck and, I am sure, brilliant surgery saved Billy's eye. I relied on Susan for periodic reports on his progress, which was sure if frustratingly slow, and I did not see him again until he returned to school about seven weeks later. When I did meet him, I was both astounded and dismayed by his unkempt appearance and, in particular, by the length of his hair. Clearly, he had not been inside a barber's shop since a month before his accident. To describe his bright red locks as shoulder length would have been a gross understatement and their colour made things even worse.

At Lea Grange, we had basic requirements regarding dress and personal appearance of which I reminded Billy promptly and in no uncertain terms. His response left me speechless. He liked his hair as it was and he had no intention of having it cut. Somewhere along the line, the school's petty 'regulations' were mentioned. I quickly terminated our exchanges and ordered him to report to me at four o'clock. I sat down to consider how to deal with this difficult situation. It was clear that he was trading on our previous good relationship as well as my friendship with his mother and my obvious affection for his lovely dog. The proverb 'Familiarity breeds contempt' came to mind even though my close relationship with the family had developed solely for his well-being. I was faced with a text-book dilemma: either I give in to him and let his glowing tresses signal to all and sundry that the school's rules on appearance no longer matter or I come down heavily on him and thus destroy our relationship and perhaps ruin all the progress we have made in his personal development. His mother's position also had to be considered: suspending Billy would hurt her more than it hurt him.

As things turned out, I was thrown a life-line. Just before school closed for the day a very angry Head of Art came to see me. "I've caught Billy Gregory with this box of pastels in his case. He says he was only borrowing them but I don't believe him. Two boxes have already gone missing this month," he exploded.

"Sit down, Keith. Billy can't have stolen the others. He only returned to school today."

"I know that," went on Keith Jackson. "I'm not saying he did but I've caught him red-handed this time. Make an example of him and the stealing will stop."

Ten minutes later an unusually truculent, uncooperative and unrepentant boy stood before me. He complained that I should know better than to accuse him of stealing and, incidentally, there was no way that I or anyone else would make him have a hair cut. I was about to guillotine our verbal parrying when the 'phone rang. It was the local fire-brigade chief calling to arrange an inspection of our appliances.

"Hello Inspector," I said, looking straight at Billy, "how convenient of you to telephone at this moment" The fire chief's puzzled response was lost to me as Billy shot forward and uttered, in a stage whisper, "Don't tell him, Sir. I've already had a warning from the police last week about riding my moped. Sir, I'll do anything if you don't tell him." There was no point in informing Billy that I was speaking to the Fire Brigade and not the Police.

"Hello, Inspector. Sorry, the line seems to be faulty. Please replace your receiver and I'll call you back." I turned my attention to Billy. "You'll do anything! Right, here's two shillings: go and get your hair cut, short back and sides, and bring me the change. I'll be here till six o'clock."

The fire inspection was arranged before Billy returned, duly shorn. I didn't expect him ever to forgive me and I'm sorry to say that things were never the same during his remaining months in school. He obtained three 'O' levels: Art, Language and Literature. I lost touch with both him and Susan so, when I met him at a funeral, eight years later, he took me completely by surprise. "Hello, Sir. Pity about Derek. He was reckless on that motor-bike!" Further small talk ensued, then, "Sir, I want to apologise to you for all the trouble I caused you. I realise now, just how you put yourself out for me. I bet you can't guess what I'm doing now!"

"I've no idea. I give up. What, in fact, are you up to?"

"I'm in my final year of teacher training."

"Amazing" I couldn't avoid a smile. "The poacher has turned game-keeper. At least you'll know all the tricks and be a step ahead of the villains."

"Yes, just like you, Sir!" His impertinent response was tempered by his irresistible grin.

CHAPER 7

"LUST IN THE DUST"

**"for 'tis the sport to have the engineer
hoist with his own petar."**

W SHAKESPEARE 1564-1616

Like everyone else in the western world, perhaps even the whole world, I have no difficulty in remembering where I was when the life of John F Kennedy, the American President, was so abruptly and cruelly terminated. I had returned to school that evening to meet Albert Crompton, a fellow headmaster, when our deliberations were interrupted by Bill Brown, the school keeper, who had heard the tragic news on his portable radio. I don't think either of us realised the full implications of the world's loss because, after a few exchanges of sadness and mild shock, we resumed the purpose of our liaison, which was to devise how the case of a promising young teacher, who had been guilty of a romantic indiscretion, should be handled.

I valued greatly the advice and friendship of Albert Crompton, a head of some fifteen years' experience. Respectively nicknamed, indeed, respectfully, nicknamed, either 'The Mule' or 'Pickwick', he possessed unlimited stores of common-sense. The first nick-name was an obvious play on the name of an eighteenth century invention but, of more importance, it was a concise and apt description of his disposition. "I don't give in, Mr Firestone, when I know I'm right: and I usually am!" More often that not, his opinions were sound and his decisions were sensible and fair so his stubbornness, far from attracting criticism, was generally perceived as wisdom and strength.

The alternative pseudonym, 'Pickwick', related unequivocally to his appearance. Middle-aged, short and broad in stature, with soft pink cheeks framed by brown sideburns, he did personify the eponymous Dickensian character. I never saw Albert wearing a matching suit. Of course, he always wore a jacket, a vest and a pair of trousers but although the former two garments were usually from the same cloth, the trousers were invariably of a different material. Rumour had it that this eccentric trait reflected a frugal streak: usually trousers wear out before the matching jacket and waist-coat and, in Albert's case, it was cheaper to buy a pair of trousers rather than a new suit. Again, this quirk in his character was generally treated with good humour rather than derision. I never heard anyone ridicule him even though some would-be comedians on his staff occasionally indulged themselves with such jibes as: "Have you heard the latest? Pickwick's been arrested for breaking into a five pound note!"

So here I was sitting comfortably with this fount of wisdom, whose advice I genuinely valued and respected. In retrospect, I suppose that his philosophy of management rested on three main premises: always be fair and just; never make a decision in a hurry; and never compromise yourself with a member of the opposite sex. Indeed, the purpose of our meeting was to examine ways of extricating a young teacher from an indiscretion in the latter category and Albert was about to describe just how serious the consequences of such foolish behaviour can be.

Before embarking on his cautionary tale, he related an incident in which, he claimed, he had been involved recently. I only have his word for its veracity but it is worth repeating just for its audacious humour. I have no difficulty in confirming the truth of its beginning in that, a couple of weeks earlier, I and all the other local head-teachers had received a questionnaire from county headquarters, which had allegedly been drawn up by the chief education officer.

Many colleagues and I had experienced difficulty in compiling answers to some of the questions which we found to be, at the best ambiguous and, at the worst, incomprehensible. In fact, I still had some sections to complete even though the closing date for replies had passed.

Albert's approach to what he considered a waste of time had been both positive and aggressive. He had stayed on at school one night earlier in the week to finish a task which he felt had hung over him for too long. Around six o'clock, still unable to decipher the meaning of several questions, he telephoned the education department at county hall. Unusually, he was greeted by a male operator.

"Yes, this is county hall."

"May I speak to someone in the education department."

"You are through to the education department but the staff left at five thirty."

Albert persevered. "Never mind the staff. Will you tell the chief education officer from me that this form he has sent to the headteachers is a load of rubbish. He calls himself an expert: I doubt whether he could organise a chocolate club!" There followed a definite pause.

"Do you realise who you are talking to?"

Albert: "No, and I don't bloody well care."

"Well, I'll tell you. You are speaking to the chief education officer: the very one who is incapable of running a chocolate club."

There followed an even longer lull in the conversation, then Albert asked, "Do you realise who you are speaking to?"

The chief education officer replied, "No, you didn't give me your name."

"Thank God for that," said Albert as he hastily replaced the instrument.

I shook my head in disbelief. "That's about on a par with your clanger when you were helping at the diagnostic centre." Albert's face gave nothing away. "It's as true as I sit here." He then added, "Both stories are the gospel truth."

I was certain that he had greatly embellished his story about the diagnostic centre because our pupils were heavily involved with supportive work for the thirty or so maladjusted children who continually passed through and, consequently, I was in close touch with the warden. When I referred casually to Albert's tale he was unable to recall any such occurrence. I had realised for some time that Albert's anecdotes, specially the humorous variety, must be taken with a pinch of salt.

Thus, when he commenced the tale to illustrate the perils of sexual indiscretion, I was suitably on my guard. From my point of view, it had an unusual theme in that it was not about chasing recalcitrant children in search of justice: it was about a rogue headteacher receiving his just deserts.

At the outset, Albert assured me that the man involved was unknown to me and that, in fact, the whole episode had occurred in a district miles away from where we were operating. That established, he had no misgivings about describing the full personal and private details of the affair: for the same reasons, I feel no restraint in doing likewise.

For convenience, Albert chose Sean as the fellow's nom de plume. Sean was head of a large primary school, situated in a socially advantaged area. Parental support was of the highest level: consequently the school enjoyed an excellent reputation and places were eagerly sought after.

The success was due in no small measure to Sean's personality, ability and enthusiasm. Just under six feet tall, with broad shoulders and a slim waist, very good looking, he was extremely popular with females of all ages ranging from kids of seven up to their grandmothers.

He was very conscious of his assets and, prior to the infamous episode, it could be said that he used them to full advantage whilst always having regard for temperance, restraint and sobriety. This was not to say that he was unaware of the temptations that daily passed before him: grateful young mothers; deferential young teachers; and, indeed, many females who had cause to visit his school for all kinds of reasons. At least he was very fortunate that his secretary, although quietly attractive, appeared to be happily married and content with their formal working relationship, which was based on mutual trust and respect. It was to the small office which he shared with this stable assistant and confidante that he could retreat with complete confidence and security.

Four weeks before the Christmas break, Sean's school was the subject of a full inspection by a team of Her Majesty's Inspectors. Although the written report of the visit was not due until the following January, the chairman of the panel had given the headmaster and staff a verbal account of what it would contain. They were assured that they had every reason for pride and satisfaction.

In view of this good news, it was decided that the usual staff Christmas party that year would be a very special affair. On the last afternoon of term after all the children had departed the premises, champagne corks popped and Sean and his loyal band of teachers plunged earnestly into the business of celebration. Fears of the clamp down on driving with excess alcohol did not cross his mind. Why should such worries spoil the pleasure he deserved when his faithful secretary, Gina, had offered to drive him home after the party ended?

As the evening wore on and the stack of empty bottles grew, members of staff began to tear themselves away from the revels and, eventually, two people were left: Sean and Gina. Albert spared me the details of the next stage of the episode by simply repeating Sean's assertion that Gina seduced him on the staff room table. He was drunk and he was certain that he would not have succumbed to temptation had he been sober.

Sean remembered little of his car journey home. He was soon asleep in his bed and as the dreadful realisation struck him when he awoke next morning, he consoled himself in the knowledge that Gina had a happy marriage and that she was unlikely to risk it by talking to anyone about their joint lapse. Admittedly, he was uneasy whenever the telephone bell rang during the first few days of the holidays but, after a week of no communication with either Gina or her husband, he felt safe and almost back to normal. Indeed, in this relatively secure state he could occasionally indulge himself by savouring the violent passion he had enjoyed with his hitherto prim and proper subordinate.

Of course, the acid test of his position would become plain when the school reopened after Christmas and he came face to face with Gina. When the fateful morning did arrive, he could not have been more reassured. His secretary was her normal polite and efficient self, looking more attractive to him than in the past, it's true, but he put this down to his changed perception of her as the result of the intimacy they had shared at the party.

Thus Sean was completely unprepared for what happened immediately after the dinner break when the children and teachers were safely back in their class-rooms hard at work. As he perused a set of third year pupils' test results, deriving satisfaction from the high standards they had attained, Gina's perfume gradually pervaded his senses. She had moved quietly across the room to a position almost behind his chair but to his left. As he turned towards her she pressed her mouth against his and slowly insinuated her bottom on to his lap.

In retrospect, Sean recognised that moment as the most significant of his career, perhaps of his whole life. Once he had recovered from the initial shock of finding Gina in his arms, clearly offering herself to him, his brain should have taken control. That was the time to say no to himself and no to Gina. That was the time to point out that their earlier lapse had been the result of too much alcohol. It must not happen again: working in such close proximity would be impossible unless they took a firm hold on themselves.

Thus, he cannot explain how and why he allowed Gina to take his hand and lead him into his en-suite wash room. He was perfectly sober, he loved his wife and children, and he was quite clear about the grave difficulties he was walking into. Most of all though, he was flattered, he was excited and he was unable to resist temptation.

Gina worked part-time on three days each week which was just as well considering the regularity with which they indulged themselves as soon as school re-commenced after each daily dinner break. At first, Sean regretted that he and his lover saw each other only on three occasions each week but, after a month or so, he was looking forward to the fallow days. Inevitably, his work suffered: he was aware of this and it troubled him.

One afternoon, on one of Gina's non-working days, as he sat at his desk pondering how he could wave a wand and return their relationship to its original wholesome state, his door opened abruptly and a smartly dressed fellow, whom he recognised vaguely, strode in. Sean was soon aware of the identity of his intruder.

"What makes you think you can fornicate with my wife and get away with it?"

"Please close the door." Sean was in deep trouble and he was already wondering how he could contain it. The exchange was remarkably short. Any further misconduct would result in dire consequences was the fundamental message. On the plus side, there was no mention of relaying the matter either to his employers or, even worse, to his wife. On the minus side, there was no suggestion that Gina should give up her job.

In fact, she reported earlier than usual next day. Sean began, "I think you owe me an explanation."

"I'm sorry it had to be you. I am genuinely very fond of you, still am, but I was desperate."

"I'm not following you."

Gina was clearly upset: on the verge of tears. "Just before Christmas I discovered that my husband was seeing one of the young girls in his office after work. He's old enough to be her father!"

Sean shook his head in disbelief. It was his turn to be near to tears. "You used me to batter him!".

"I said I'm sorry. You're a very nice guy. You deserve better." That was all. They looked at each other for several minutes then Sean suggested that she should get on with the typing he had given her.

He knew that things would never be quite the same as before but he hoped that time would do the proverbial healing. Sadly he was to be disappointed, nay devastated. Just one week after his original visit, Gina's husband walked into Sean's study, again without knocking. "Just checking you and my wife aren't up to no good," and he was gone. Regular visits continued over the next two or three months, always on the days when Gina was not working. The fellow did not always burst into the room: sometimes he appeared at the window and moved away again once he had assured himself that Sean was aware of his presence. The visits were never referred to either by Sean or Gina.

Just when he felt he could tolerate the pressure no longer, a solution emerged. Gina informed him that she intended to apply for the full-time secretarial post at the local grammar school, which would be available the following September. She was not unhappy in her present post but she felt she needed a challenge and a new full time job would provide it.

Sean attempted to hide his elation. They exchanged platitudes relating to the length of excellent service she had given and how a change of situation would be beneficial to her. She would be very sorry to leave and he would be very sorry to lose her.

The formalities connected with her application got off to a promising start when she was summoned for interview and when, concurrently, Sean was asked to supply a confidential reference on her behalf. Realising that her departure would solve his problems and present him with a new start, he set about his task with enthusiasm but also with great care. He changed his rough draft twice before he was anywhere near to being satisfied, then he turned his attention to the conclusion. Somehow he had to convey to the interviewing panel that it would be madness for them to consider appointing anybody but Gina. He concluded his magnificent eulogy with words to the effect that he knew he would never find another secretary as good as she. He went even further, if she ever wanted her job back it would be hers for the asking. Suitably satisfied, he sealed the envelope, posted it himself and impatiently waited for its contents to do their work.

Gina telephoned him at home on the evening of the interview to share the good news. He effected surprise at hearing from her and thanked her for letting him be "the first to know." He did not admit that he had heard the result three hours earlier, having casually enquired "out of interest" at the divisional education office.

On her last afternoon of term, having cleared her desk, Gina prepared to leave. Sean courteously stood and, face to face, offered her his hand.

"Just one last kiss, please," said Gina, placing her hands on his shoulders, Why not? In five minutes she would be part of his past. Her hand was soon on the door handle. She turned, "I love you, Sean. Why can't I have you instead of that beast?"

"Go now, Gina. You must. I'll always have a place for you in my heart."

She was gone. He was glad, relieved, drained. He was pleased that he had not told her he loved her. He wondered if he had been too effusive as it was. What of it? She had another job, she was gone and she wouldn't be back. A very uncomfortable chapter of his life was over.

He spent the last three weeks of the summer holidays camping in Scotland with his two sons whilst his wife paid her annual visit to her mother on the south coast. This was why the divisional education officer was unable to contact Sean, even though he and his staff tried several times each day. It would be a formality, the official told himself. He just needed Sean's agreement to re-instate Gina as his secretary. Apparently, during the first weeks of the holiday she had given the matter a lot of thought and reached the conclusion that she already had a good job. She could never hope to obtain the same satisfaction anywhere else and so she was asking permission to withdraw from her new post and stay in her present position. No mention was made of her feelings for Sean.

As time drew near for schools to reopen, the divisional education officer decided that he must make the decision. To assist him, he consulted his office file on Gina and turned to Sean's recently compiled confidential report. Amazingly, the conclusion covered just the situation that existed. Unable to consult Sean, the official exercised his prerogative and a grateful Gina was instructed to report to her hero on the first day of the autumn term. A copy of the letter of re-appointment was awaiting Sean when he arrived home from his camping trip, One particular sentence made him weep. "In view of the excellent confidential report submitted by your present headteacher, I have no hesitation in agreeing to your continuing in your present post at his school." Sean had been hoisted by his own petard.

"I don't believe it! It's incredible!" I repeated.

"Incredible but true," Albert replied.

"What happened to him?"

"You might well ask. Within a month he had applied for and obtained an advisory post with another education authority and, no more was heard of him.

"So where does that leave us with our problem?" I enquired.

"It's obvious: the lad should move on, start afresh. He hasn't any roots here, has he?"

"I'm sure you're right, Albert. If he stays, he'll never be quite at ease. In this close-knit area, somebody's bound to find out and spill the beans."

"That's settled then," said Albert. "Have a word with him tomorrow. Come on, if we hurry we'll have time for a quick pint."

It goes without saying that Albert had trouble with his car lock outside the Rose and Crown and there was just time for me to order before the pumps were covered.

"Cheers, my turn next time," lied Albert.

I did not need to send for the young teacher next morning. He was eagerly awaiting my arrival. "I hope you don't mind. Mr Firestone, I've decided to accept a librarian post in the midlands! I'd like to apply for an early release."

Had Albert and I wasted our time the previous evening? I had not: it had been most entertaining and rewarding, even though I did buy the drinks.

CHAPTER 8

"PERSONAL MISUNDERSTANDINGS"

**"O wad some pow'r the giftie gie us
to see oursels as others see us"**

ROBERT BURNS 1858-1943

Not being able to see the wood for the trees is generally attributed either to the congenitally narrow minded, who are either unwilling or unable to consider opinions contrary to their own, or to just plain and simple dreamers. Certainly the charge should never apply to one who considers himself to be alert, intelligent, astute, even cunning when necessary, and always a step ahead of the most devious pupils in his care. Yet, on several embarrassing occasions, whilst headmaster of Lea Grange, there is no doubt that I was guilty of such self delusion.

I hasten to add that my faux pas tended to occur in my personal life rather than whilst I was about my duties. Perhaps I was so keen to be in control at school that in the comparative tranquillity of my private life, my awareness and perception fell to an abysmally low level. Among the many occasions when I succeeded in completely misreading a set of circumstances, I remember two as being particularly embarrassing at the time, even if the intervening years now enable me to look back upon them with no little amusement.

I take some satisfaction from the knowledge that blunders are not my sole preserve and that even the most shrewd of persons can labour under a misapprehension. In this respect, I recall an incident related to me by Albert Crompton, to which I have already referred and, I feel obliged to add, the truth of which I still doubt. Nevertheless, it is an excellent example of how failing to see oneself as others see us can deal a severe blow to one's dignity. It is worth repeating.

Albert claimed that the incident occurred whilst he was visiting his friend, who was in charge of a residential diagnostic centre for maladjusted boys and girls. I had no difficulty in picturing the scene as I and my staff were closely involved with the centre, a majestic stone-built residence which stood in acres of woodland. It catered for about thirty children of varying ages, whose average stay was about one month, sometimes less and occasionally longer. Consequently, there was never a settled community and friendships among the children had little time to develop. Care and attention from visitors were gratefully welcomed and it was in such circumstances that we had developed a link with the unit. Every evening, three or four senior girls would attend to assist with the bed-time ritual: bathing the youngsters; helping them to put on their pyjamas; and finally, settling them down for the night with a story or just a cuddle. Sometimes the antics were almost too hilarious to be believed but it was always a happy occasion, greatly looked forward to by our girls and their little charges.

The contribution made by our boys was just as useful if less spectacular. Again, small groups attended on a regular basis taking with them toys to occupy the little ones, particular favourites being kites, model gliders and action men.

Of course, our girls and boys appreciated being treated like adults by the head of the centre. Richard was a giant in all respects. Standing well above six feet in his tartan shirt, corduroy trousers and slip-on brogues, he exuded warmth and security. He was sensitive, patient and caring: ideally suited to undertake his worthy duties. His wife, Helen, much smaller in stature but equally equipped in all other respects, was a perfect partner in their important work and I believe their friendly personalities were paramount in attracting helpers, adults and youngsters alike.

Our children especially enjoyed experimenting with the two-way mirror, which connected Richard's office with the main indoor play area, and of course, the final event of the evening, which consisted of a light supper at the large oak kitchen table.

It was then that they would discuss the events of the evening and Richard would intrigue them with accounts of case histories of anonymous children who had long since passed through the centre. And, of course, they became involved in current cases. One little boy amazed us all by a most unusual ability: if he was quoted a date, for instance the tenth of January, 1925, he would immediately name the day of the week on which the quoted date had fallen; in this case it was a Saturday. He never got it wrong.

Another case was most interesting: over a period of time the permanent members of staff had become aware that a ten year old boy appeared to function three weeks in arrears. His whole conversation was confined to events that had occurred twenty-one days earlier but he spoke as if they were happening currently. The three week lapse was first spotted by a young assistant at the centre and, once the staff were aware of the situation, it was easy to identify the time lag in the little boy's thinking. In particular, his references to specific activities such as visits to the swimming baths, to the local supermarket or to day trips, all of which had occurred three weeks earlier but which he spoke of as currently occurring, confirmed his problem with chronology. One of our senior girls suggested a simple solution: administer a drug which would make him sleep for three weeks and then, when he awoke, he would have caught up. I don't think the professionals were impressed.

So, one day, Albert had been persuaded to give a talk to the two dozen little girls and boys who sat cross-legged on the polished floor of the meeting room eagerly looking up at both him and Richard, who sat comfortably in their easy chairs.

Just when our hero was beginning to enjoy listening to his own voice with the self-satisfaction of one who is used to pontificating to captive audiences, he was abruptly interrupted by a sheepish young boy who called out, "Rubbish!". A few little girls giggled and Albert's flow was momentarily stalled although he was soon back into his stride. A second interruption followed. This time, "What a load of nonsense!" was the little boy's offering. Albert's pause was longer as he looked across at his colleague for support and guidance. Richard seemed intent only on scratching his left ear and looking anywhere except in Albert's direction so, when the little gigglers, a few boys as well as the little girls this time, had composed themselves, Albert began again.

"Tommyrot, balderdash, gobbledegook!" The little boy was really warming to his theme. Albert was brought to a full stop, speechless. He looked across at Richard and waited patiently until eye contact was established. "Shall I pack it in?"

"No, no, carry on, you're doing fine. Simon's been with us for three weeks and it's the first time he's said anything remotely sensible."

I suppose if Albert was capable of telling a story about how his ego received such a salutary lesson then I should not be too despondent when I think back to my own gaffes. It really is remarkable how an initial misconception can result in a whole series of ensuing blunders. The business began one bank holiday when we discovered that we had run out of milk. We had only recently moved into a new house and we had no idea where we could obtain an emergency supply. The best bet seemed for me to run over to the milkman's home base where he was sure to have some in store. I wasn't sure of his address but I knew that his name was Bill Mathews and that he lived in the next village. A quick perusal of the telephone directory revealed the address of B.W. Matthews, in the said village, and I was soon waiting on the doorstep of a well tended bungalow.

In answer to my knock the door was opened by a sheepish young lad of about ten years.

"Does Mr Bill Matthews live here?"

"Yes, he's my dad."

"Can I have a word with him?"

"He's not in."

"Is your mother in?"

"No, they've gone over to my aunt's in Lytham."

"Oh! well look, my name's Mr Firestone and I live in Chapel Road, Beckbridge. Can you let me have a bottle of milk and I'll make it straight with your father at the weekend."

"All right, I'll go and see."

The young lad brought me a bottle of milk and I presume Bill Matthew's added it to my bill at the weekend.

Several months later we ran short of milk again. This time, it wasn't such a problem because I knew where Bill Matthews lived and there had been no difficulty on the previous occasion.

In fact, it turned out to be a case of deja vu. The same quiet little boy answered the door. Yes, he was sure it was all right for me to have another bottle of milk.

I'm sure there was no problem because, at the month end I received Bill's account and I sent him my cheque as usual.

About two years passed without further incident as far as our milk supply was concerned then, one evening, as we packed up the car to go away on holiday, I suddenly realised that we had not cancelled our milk order. I tried to telephone Bill but there was no reply from his number. Directory enquiries confirmed that there had been no alteration so, after two or three further attempts, I decided to write a short note and push it through his letter box.

As I approached the door of his bungalow, a neighbour called out to me. "Can I help you?"

"No thanks, I'm just leaving a note for Bill Matthews."

"He's in Spain, went last Saturday for two weeks."

"He can't have. He left us our milk this morning."

The helpful neighbour looked perplexed. "Left you your milk! Not this Bill Matthews: he's a foreman at the slipper works. You want William Matthews, the milkman. He lives at the other end of the village!"

Somewhat dazed and very disconsolate I journeyed to the other end of the village to deliver my instructions to Mr Matthews, the milkman and then I went on holiday. I still owe Mr Matthews, the slipper works foreman, for two bottles of milk. I can't begin to imagine the explanations that the poor little lad gave to his parents. I'm only glad that I have not heard from the police. I'm also relieved that it occurred away from Beckbridge: such stupidity would have been hard to live down if my pupils or their parents had learned of it.

I have never attempted to evaluate whether or not my other major faux pas was more or less embarrassing than my affair with the milkman. Certainly the necessary conditions to encourage over-confidence leading to self-delusion did exist because the incident occurred on an evening following a day when I had sat in court: a day when I arrived home feeling pleasantly satisfied with the way things had worked out. In particular, I was content in the certain knowledge that a trial over which I had presided had ended in a fair, just and correct result.

The case concerned a defendant who was accused of driving whilst under the influence of alcohol: according to the prosecution, very much so. The fellow opted to conduct his own defence, a task which he performed with confidence and not a little skill. He pleaded not guilty and based his case on the fact that he had consumed a pint of vinegar prior to his breath test and that it was acetic acid and not alcohol that had been responsible for the positive reading. He explained that he was a chronic sufferer from high cholesterol and that his doctor had advised him that the best way of controlling his problem was to consume one pint of vinegar daily.

There were several spectators in the public gallery and I am sure they thoroughly enjoyed the theatre of his performance: in particular, how he always seemed to have a plausible answer for the questions put to him by the prosecuting counsel. He usually introduced his replies with,

"I'm glad you've asked me that. It gives me a chance to explain the position clearly to their worships." He was, indeed, extremely courteous to the Bench without over-reaching himself. Some defendants, in their anxiety to curry

66

favour, have been known to address magistrates as "Your honourship" or "Your worshipfulness." He stopped short of such extravagance, but only just.

The trial lasted for over two hours as he strived to prove his innocence and he concluded his case with a competent plea. I am not permitted to divulge any details of the magisterial deliberations but, after due consideration, he was found guilty. Before sentence was passed, his previous record was revealed to the court and it indicated several alcohol related offences, the most recent of which was a drink driving conviction only a few months previously. He was in serious trouble and he knew it. It was then that he sought permission to offer a plea of mitigation in which he unequivocally admitted the current offence and apologised for wasting the court's time.

Thus, that evening, with the events of the afternoon still lingering in my subconciousness, in particular with the man's admission of guilt confirming the correctness of our verdict, I was no doubt in a prime state to misconceive. The possibility of fallibility never entered my thoughts.

It was early summer and the hawthorn hedge which bordered the three sides of the back garden was grossly overgrown to the extent of being embarrassingly untidy. With a residential conference almost upon me, parents' evenings looming and a great deal of planning needed for the new educational year, I could not see how I would be able to address the task before the midsummer break.

My spirits had sunk even lower as I arrived home that evening and saw a trailer full of lopped branches and hedge clippings standing outside Mrs Brown's cottage several doors along the road. My neighbours' neat and well-kept gardens would make mine look even worse.

I don't know why it took me so long to realise the solution to my problem. It was so simple. Like Mrs Brown, I would engage a man to do the job for me. In fact, I would act decisively and engage her man.

I busied myself in the front garden, lifting the odd weed and trimming the grass edges, always keeping an eye on the car and trailer, which were still parked outside Mrs Brown's, until my potential rescuer emerged, bidding farewell to the old lady over his shoulder. I had time to allow her to go inside and close her front door before I made my move because the tree lopper was busy securing a tarpaulin over the clippings.

"Good evening. You've got quite a load there."

"Yes, I'm afraid the bushes were neglected last year. I've had to do quite a lot of chopping."

He had the physique for hard work. Well over six feet, he had broad shoulders and well-developed arms. I remember noticing how clean he looked: blond hair, ruddy cheeks, large pink hands and freckled arms covered in a fuzz of fair hairs.

"I've got the same problem and I just haven't the time to tackle it," I ventured. "The front's all right but it's overgrown round the back."

"Let's have a look at it. It's fatal to let trees get out of hand." As we walked the short distance to my home I was dreading letting an expert see what a mess I was presiding over. In addition to the unkempt hedge, the flower borders were untidy and far too many weeds were emerging through the cracks of the crazy paved patio. It was not a garden to be proud of.

"Yes, I see what you mean," was my companion's under-statement. "You need some powered tools. I'll lend you mine with pleasure." It was now or never, I began,

"Actually, I was wondering if you would do the job for me."

"Hm, I don't know. There's quite a lot to do. I certainly couldn't manage anything this month."

"Well no, I should fit in with you, of course." He gave in.

"Leave it with me. I'll arrange something. I'll ring you in a couple of months."

Marvellous: I controlled my relief. As he drove off with his large load I felt that my affable friend had relieved me of an even larger one. I must do the courteous thing as soon as possible and mention it to Mrs Brown.

In fact, the opportunity presented itself the following morning. As I reversed out of my drive, the old lady was tripping purposefully by. She was her usual stylish self, clad in her blue coat and matching bonnet, and equipped with shopping basket and umbrella.

"Good morning Mrs Brown. Can I give you a lift?"

"Good morning to you, Mr Firestone. I don't think it's worth your trouble, thanks. I'm only going to the grocer's."

I was keen to tell her how I'd taken the liberty of engaging her man so I persisted. "That's fine. I've got a call to make before school so I'll be passing your shop. Come on, hop in."

As soon as we were moving, I came straight to the point. "Mrs Brown, I was talking to your gardener last night and we've arranged for him to come over and lop my trees. He seems a really good bloke. He's agreed to do it even though he's ever so busy. I hope you don't mind."

I still cringe when I think of the old lady's reply. "Oh yes, he is a really good bloke, as you put it, and I know he's very busy. Just one thing, though: he isn't my gardener, he's my son. I'm very, very proud of him, you know. He comes and does all my odd jobs even though he's the chief surgeon at the Eye Hospital!"

CHAPTER 9

"GRASPING THE NETTLE"

**"There is a tide in the affairs of men,
which, taken at the flood, leads on to fortune;
Omitted, all the voyage of their life
Is bound in shallows and in miseries......"**

W SHAKESPEARE 1564-1616

"Are you getting on any better with Parsons nowadays?"
Albert Crompton, my fellow head and friend, and I were
travelling to a meeting at County Hall. I had confided
previously to Albert that my adviser and I did not see eye to
eye on several basic issues.

"We tolerate each other." I was deliberately brief
because I did not want to spoil a pleasant journey through
the picturesque Forest of Bowland.

Albert persisted. "He's all right when you get to know
him. His problem is that he's from the south of England,
rather pretentious to say the least. Did you know his full
name is Hobbes-Parsons? He dropped the double-barrel
when he applied for a job in the north."

"Hobbes-Parsons," I echoed, "terribly, terribly
distinguished."

"Yes, well there's a story about his name," went on
Albert. I thought there would be so I braced myself for
another of my friend's bizarre anecdotes. He took a little
time to gather his thoughts into a logical order: then he
began. "Apparently, it all started when he was demobbed
from the Air Force at the end of the second world war. He
and his twin brother had both read Philosophy at Cambridge
and one night, after a few drinks, they did what many
ambitious young men do: they attempted to map out how
their careers would develop over the following forty years.
Until that night, they were just plain Parsons but one of
them devised the bright idea that, if they were to apply for

jobs in the southern counties, double-barrelled names would not go amiss."

"So?" I enquired.

"Well, as they were both philosophers, one of them suggested they should each pick the name of a well-known one and add it to his own surname. Our friend chose Hobbes, after the 'Leviathan'." Then, he added, "Not Jack, the cricketer."

"Don't patronise me Albert. What about his brother?"

"He chose Locke after the famous John." It was my turn.

"Of the American constitution: not Tony, the spin the bowler. I get the drift. Then our chap decided that a double-barrel might not go down so well up north so he conveniently dropped it when he applied to Lancashire?"

"Exactly right," conceded Albert. We drove on for some minutes in silence, enjoying the lovely rural landscape. Predictably, Albert had to speak. "So you still only tolerate each other?"

"I'm afraid so. Our experiences have been so different and, from what you have just told me, so are our attitudes."

"He knows his theory." In retrospect, I think Albert was goading me.

"That's just the point. He might have read the books: it's practice he is short of. He wouldn't last five minutes in the school where I served as deputy-head."

"Was it so bad?"

"Bad! It was unbelievable at first, although I must admit I enjoyed it once I had established myself. It was all a matter of being in control. Without control, nothing is possible. That's what I try to get Parsons to understand."

"How do you mean?"

"Well, to begin with, the kids were different. The school served a very low-grade housing estate: an estate from which aspiring families moved at the earliest opportunity only to be replaced by problem families. It was council policy: to reward good behaviour by re-locating deserving cases into better areas and moving troublesome families on to our estate."

"Presumably to confine the council's problems to a limited area," suggested Albert.

"That's right, but you can imagine what it was like for us poor devils who had to educate the off-spring." I overtook a cart laden with bales of straw and continued. "On the first morning that I, as Deputy-Head, mind you, stood before my class of forty-three fifteen year old boys, I was greeted with a continuous humming of Colonel Bogey accompanied by feet stamping to the refrain. The noise continued for several minutes whilst I stood at the front attempting to make eye contact with my tormentors. Well practised in the art of disruption, they stared down at their desks and kept up the pressure. It was unnerving: utterly different from driving along country lanes like we are doing. Suddenly, a boy called out, 'Give the gentleman a minute!' My relief was short-lived. Before I could utter a word he announced, 'Minute's up.' The noise resumed at an even louder pitch. I knew my survival was threatened and I wasn't prepared to let that mob ruin my career. Using my full height and strength, I yanked the self-styled comic out of his desk and roughly pinned him against the wall. I'm sure I hurt him but I was pretty desperate. He was petrified, thank God! Another boy called out, 'Leave him alone, his dad's a boxer!' They all laughed but then fell silent. I noticed that two boys on the front row had placed heavily-buckled belts across their desks. I said, 'Put them back on: your trousers will fall down.' A tense period followed whilst we attempted to out-stare each other. I took a couple of steps towards them, keeping up my steady gaze. To my relief, first one and then the other dropped his eyes and re-buckled his belt in place."

"Nobody should have to work in those conditions," Albert observed sympathetically.

"That's true but many splendid men and women had been existing there long before I joined the school. The problem was that the Headteacher had little authority. Having experienced such conditions makes me determined to keep a tight control at Lea Grange."

"I bet you were glad to leave," said Albert.

"Believe it or not, Albert, I was sorry when the time came. You see, once I had established my position, I really enjoyed my work there. It was a combination of teacher and social worker: a tremendous challenge but extremely rewarding. In fact, when I got to know the kids, I really liked them. But they were different." Several images came to mind as we drove along.

"There was George who appeared one day in a pair of jeans into which he had tightly sewn his legs. 'How can you possibly have a bath? You can't get them off,' I said. He just grinned as if to say, 'Who said anything about having baths?'

Then there was Dorothy, a sweet natured girl who suffered from the worst body-odour my nostrils have ever encountered. I say she suffered: actually, it was her class mates and I who suffered the most. The only way I could think of to minimise the problem was to ensure that she never sat in direct sunlight. To make matters worse, she never stayed away. All the kids were the same: they preferred school to home, where they had to do all the chores. As I said before, once I was in control, there was plenty to laugh about. I remember an afternoon break being taken up by Falstaff, the Head of English. Falstaff was his nick-name: you can guess why, He was the calmest man I have ever known: quiet, courteous and measured but always in control. I never heard him utter an oath. According to him, swearing revealed a lack of facility with one's native language. Certainly, English contains enough suitable adjectives to enable one to describe his feelings without the need to resort to profanity and blasphemy. Of course, his nick-name was derived from his girth rather than his character. That particular afternoon he had just completed a vocabulary period on words relating to destruction. He vowed that he could not recall a class ever taking so much interest in a lesson. Apparently they were a veritable thesaurus of disaster although, of course, they were unable to spell most of their offerings: pulverise, disintegrate, annihilate, cruelty, mince, decompose, murder, torture and mutilate. They did throw in a few words they were able to spell such as crush, smash and mash. Violence had a natural attraction for them: a compulsive fascination is the best way I can describe it. In one form, all the boys but one were on probation and the odd one out was the biggest rogue of all. It goes without saying that all one's personal belongings had to be carefully guarded and a specially re-inforced stock room was set aside for all valuable equipment.

No level of behaviour seemed too outrageous for them. One group's favourite diversion was to set fire to the box of shavings in the wood-work room, much to the chagrin of the poor old teacher, who must have been counting the months to his retirement. Tall and thin with a bald head and a brown smock, he was the personification of the Giles cartoon character. When Falstaff asked the boys why they persisted in such anti-social activity he was informed, 'We're not trying to burn the school down. It's just that we like to see Chalky jump into the box to stamp out the flames. He looks like an Indian Chief doing a war-dance round the camp fire'.

"I can't imagine why you stayed in such an awful place," observed Albert.

"Ambition, I suppose" I replied. "To throw in the towel would have marked me as a quitter. I would have had to wave goodbye to ever becoming a Headmaster. Anyway, somebody had to work there."

We drove on in silence for a mile or two.

"The worst experience I had at the school eventually rebounded in my favour and enabled me to establish myself firmly in control once and for all. Looking back, I rate it as possibly the most significant event of my career."

"Tell me more," said Albert. Listening to someone else's tales was an almost unique experience for my companion but I had him securely hooked and I intended to make the most of it. "Come on, Adam, the full story, please."

"Well," I began, "it all started one Monday morning before assembly. Our worthy leader (as he was referred to by my fellow members of staff) called me into his study to inform me that he was too ill to remain in school. As I had held my post of deputy-head for only four weeks, I detected that he was apprehensive about leaving me in sole charge. He was obviously quite ill and I insisted that he should return home. 'It will either make me or break me,' I clearly remember observing."

"And did it?" asked Albert, clearly impatient.

"Be quiet for once and listen. I've hardly started. In fact, things proceeded almost normally for the first three days. However, at about nine o'clock on the Wednesday evening, I received a 'phone call at home informing me that there had been a riot in the school a couple of hours earlier. The problem had started at the play-centre, which ran in the school from five until seven every evening. Two young boys were enjoying a game of snooker when the school bully, who was much older than they, decided to have fun by spoiling theirs. The master in charge of the games room was a young probationer with a pale face and a quiet disposition. His appearance was anything but aggressive.

Predictably, when he politely asked the bully to behave and let the young lads get on with their game the lout challenged him to make him. I said the young man's appearance was not aggressive. What nobody knew, and especially the bully, was that a well-conditioned body, developed through long hard hours of weight-training, was concealed under his loose-fitting sports jacket.

The bully was soon on the wrong end of a half-nelson and, to the delight of his many victims, was summarily ejected from the premises in a most undignified manner."

"Serve the bugger right," observed Albert.

"Yes but unfortunately it didn't end there. In the usual cowardly way that bullies act, this one gathered about twenty teenagers, lads who had left school two or three years earlier and persuaded them to return to the play-centre to beat up the young teacher. I don't know what lies he had fed to them but, by all accounts, they were very fired up, armed with bicycle chains and hunks of wood bearing down upon the school with chants of 'We want Clarence', which was the unfortunate teacher's nick-name. On hearing their approach, the Head of the play-centre locked the external doors and called the police. The arrival of two squad cars persuaded the mob to disperse and order was quickly restored."

"So no real harm came of it." said Albert.

"Don't you believe it. Clarence was in a terrible state of shock, really distressed. His colleagues did not expect him to set foot in the building ever again."

"And did he?"

"He certainly did. In fact, the next morning he reported at the same time as I did: a good half-hour before our normal time of arrival. He waited for me at the gate and we walked together past a group of boys who grew silent and sullen as we approached."

'Morning boys.'

'Morning Sirs.' Lines of communication were still open.

That morning, it was the turn of the Junior Department to use the assembly hall so I had no way of gauging the mood of the school as a whole. The only certainty was that everyone knew about the previous night's riotous happenings.

At a quarter past nine the school secretary informed me that the Director of Education wanted me on the 'phone. He had two concerns: was I in charge of the situation; and, secondly, was I aware that no statements must be given to the media? I think the second concern was uppermost in his mind. With an eye on my future, I assured him that I had already taken full control. Everything was normal and any overtures from the press would be firmly rebuffed.

In fact, I was soon carrying out the latter undertaking. By ten thirty, a young reporter accompanied by a tubby little man with a camera, who had slipped quietly on to the premises, almost bumped into me as I stepped out of the head's study. My anxiety about the predicament we were in must have been mistaken by them for rage, which could only result in physical harm to them, for they left immediately after I had only uttered a dozen words."

"What did you say? was Albert's inevitable question.

"What the bloody hell do you two think you are up to? I'm not having the press trespassing in my school? Unfortunately for them, morning break had just begun and several pupils witnessed the short incident. By the time the two budding journalists had descended the stairs to the outside door a loyal band of supporters, mostly from my form, was waiting to hasten their departure from the grounds. This encouragement proved most effective and the two intruders were soon driving furiously away from the school in their V.W. beetle, which had collected, I am ashamed to say, several dents caused by the stones of their pursuers.

I was both heartened and dismayed. The kids' and my common hostility towards those who were after a story to boost their sales at our expense drew us closer together. However, it was obvious that it would not take many more such incidents for me to have a very nasty situation on my hands.

My fears were confirmed immediately the school broke for lunch. I had hardly completed my midday meal in the dining room, which was a short walk across a hard playing area, when an excited young girl came in to tell me that a number of men were offering the kids pound notes to tell them what happened last night 'in their own words'. I remember thinking that things couldn't get any worse. I was right: we had hit rock bottom and we could only move upwards. In fact, what followed proved to be most significant for the well-being of the school, and it didn't do any harm to my standing or prospects.

As I stepped outside the dining hall my first impression was a distant view of several men and one woman on the school perimeter with out-stretched hands offering money as if they were in attendance at an evangelical church rally. Next, in the foreground, I was accosted by a small thin man in a striped suit with very large lapels and trilby hat, clutching a note-pad. Immediately behind him was an old-fashioned camera tripod manned by a short man in leather jacket and matching cap.

'Just a couple of shots for the Messenger: you and a group of the kids,' was the reporter's opening gambit, whilst his colleague waved a few of our pupils towards me.

'The only shots you'll get are from my toe up your backside,' was my less than erudite reply as I picked up the tripod and held it horizontally aloft. In this fashion, I strode to the boundary gate, accompanied by a group of cheering children, and made as if to fling the whole contraption into the roadway. 'Don't Sir, please,' implored leather jacket, who had hurried behind me, caught up among the menacing youngsters. 'Take it and think yourselves lucky I haven't smashed it over your head.' Even louder cheers erupted as the two intrepid news-seekers hurried away.

Am I boring you, Albert?"

"No way: then what happened?" My companion had never kept quiet for such a long period.

"Well, next, the kids decided to demonstrate against the press. In those days, the girls and boys had separate play areas. The girls had filed through the inter-connecting wicket gate and joined the boys. About four hundred of them were seated on the hard asphalt base chanting, 'Down with the press, down with the press, up with the teachers and down with the press!' At the time the noise first erupted, I was chatting to Ben, the Head of Maths.

'Oh no!' I exclaimed, 'we can't allow this.' He offered me an excellent piece of advice. 'Tackle them on your own. They'll back down if you appear confident and in charge. If you sort out the boys, I'll usher the girls back into their own playground.' I shall always be grateful to Ben for his advice and support. He was a stalwart: a man among men. Although greying prematurely, he had a young, shining face. His powerful stature exuded power and strength. His instructions to his pupils were executed without question. I followed his advice. It was easy. My approach was greeted by cheering and clapping followed by silence as I stood to address the gathering. Entry into classes was unusually orderly and I was soon expressing myself to my loyal registration group of older boys: words to the effect that, unless we exercised some self-discipline and control, the school would acquire such a low reputation that no employers would consider any of its leavers, including them. My sermon lasted for ten solid minutes and they sat perfectly still. They were impressed. The school centre-half spoke, 'We never looked at it like that, Sir, Thee put some work on t' board and go and talk like that to t'other classes. Nobody will mess about while you're out: I'll see to that.'

In Julius Caesar, Cassius had said:

'There is a tide in the affairs of men,

which, taken at the flood, leads on to fortune;

Omitted, all the voyage of their life

Is bound in sorrows and in miseries..."

I followed the centre-half's apt advice, visited all the senior classes and school closed peacefully that afternoon.

The local press had the proverbial field day. 'Riot at Black-Board jungle' was emblazoned across the front page of the evening edition. The text began, 'This morning, whilst investigating last night's riot, I was almost stoned to death, just managing to escape in my small car, which bears the scars of the attack....and so on.' Next morning, several national dailies gave space on their front pages, their reports being anything but complimentary to the school and its inmates.

To add fuel to the flames, the governing body was due to meet in the school that afternoon. We shared the committee with three other schools, including a prestigious grammar school, and the three Heads were also due to visit for their meetings. I conducted a brisk morning assembly, briefly repeating what I had said to the senior classes the previous afternoon. Finally, I invoked Cassius's maxim, informing the whole school that the visit of the governors plus three Headteachers presented us with a wonderful opportunity to prove our real worth rather than what the newspapers had written about us.

'Is it safe to come to your school?' During the morning, I shrugged off this question over the telephone on four occasions: thrice from each of my Head-teacher colleagues and once from the clerk of the governors. In fact, that afternoon, the kids were wonderful. When they filed out of the mid-session break and when they departed at four o'clock they were unbelievably quiet. The Head of the grammar school remarked that he wished his pupils were as well-behaved."

"Remarkable," said Albert, "you grasped your opportunity with both hands."

"That's true. From then on, I was in full control and we enjoyed steady improvements in all areas: attitude; progress; exam results and sporting achievements. But it could all have gone horribly wrong. Prompt and consistent action was needed over two tense days. Sitting theorising would not have brought home the bacon. I had to get out front, show leadership and provide a continuous and reassuring presence."

"All right, Adam, you've made your point. Now, there's a nice little pub in the next village: The Railway and Bicycle. Pull in there and I'll buy you a pint." He really must have been impressed!

CHAPTER 10

"THE ARSONIST"

"Desperate Diseases Require Desperate Remedies"

GUY FAWKES 1570-1606

Rupert was strange rather than wicked yet, if he had not been stalled, his activities could have resulted in the most calamitous consequences that I could ever have experienced. In his case, an urgent and decisive remedy was demanded. It is a chilling coincidence that it was Guy Fawkes who coined the phrase: "Desperate diseases require desperate remedies."

The need for prompt and effective action became apparent when John Sims, our Head of Chemistry, became convinced that materials and equipment were being systematically removed from his store-room, which, incidentally, he kept locked at all times. As is often the case, his suspicions began with a hunch that all was not as he had left it. He felt sure that his bottles of chemicals had been disturbed. On some mornings, he was surprised to find traces of different powders on his work bench and on adjacent areas of the floor. One day, he missed a pestle and mortar.

It was unfortunate for the burglar that John Sims was a particularly resourceful gentleman. He had spent most of the World War 2 in naval intelligence and it was his imaginative and inventive mind that had secured him his commission in the first place. On numerous occasions I have heard him recount the episode which catapulted him from able seaman to a high ranking officer. Early in the war, he was stationed at a land-based storage depot somewhere in rural Wales. Less than a dozen ratings, none of whom came anywhere near to approaching his intellectual level, and John were commanded by a junior officer who had recently married and who had arranged for his bride to lodge at the one pub in the village, seven miles away.

John soon tired of the two diversions on offer: snooker and darts. Although his fellow seamen were agreeable fellows, he desperately longed for stimulating conversation on subjects other than association football and acquiescent women.

Just when he felt that he could tolerate the boredom no longer, a modicum of light relief entered his life and, indeed the lives of all the men on the depot. The officer commanding the main station, of which John's unit was a satellite, decreed that all ratings were entitled to a daily tot of rum against the particularly cold winter. As the depot's young officer tended to spend more time in the village inn with his wife than on his official duties, he entrusted the security of the liquor store to John.

Inevitably, one very cold night as John lay on his bunk reading and smoking, his mind kept wandering to the easily accessible elixir that lay behind the stout oak door of which he possessed the key. He convinced himself that a nineteen year old able and fit young man deserved a better life than he was enduring and fifteen minutes later, having stoked up the internal combustion stove and imbibed a double rum, his mental attitude towards his situation had been transformed.

His heavy slumbers were abruptly interrupted at about two o'clock in the morning. He awoke to loud banging, shouting and a volcano, which had been the end wall of his hut when he had fallen asleep. Fortunately, nobody was injured and the fire was soon brought under control. Nevertheless John was going to have some explaining to do, as was the young officer, of course, who was effectively absent without leave.

They were both summoned by their commanding officer and John was given twenty-four hours to compile a written report, explaining the cause of the tragic occurrence. It was then that his fertile and inventive brain came to his assistance, in the short term saving him from a spell in a place of correction and, in the long term, ensuring a high level naval career commensurate with his ability.

He was almost certain that he had caused the fire, having fallen asleep with a lighted cigarette and half a tumbler of rum at his side. Fortunately, he remembered that, a month or so previously, he had reported a crack in the cast iron of the stove and he decided to lay the blame on that inanimate object, which was incapable of contradicting his account. It was this plausible explanation which saved him from a court-martial but it was his literary flair which brought the additional reward of rapid promotion. In his report, he avoided the use of the word 'fire', instead substituting words such as 'conflagration', 'eruption', 'furnace', and 'incendiary'. Finally, he checked the report carefully to avoid spelling or grammatical mistakes and then he persuaded the depot clerk to type it out.

"Come in, Sims. Most unfortunate business. This report, very impressive. Have you ever considered applying for a commission? The navy is crying out for people of your calibre" and so on. John was at attention in front of the C.O., having complied with the order to submit his report. The wheels of officialdom soon turned and he spent the rest of the war in relative comfort, using his considerable talent to assist in the defeat of Hitler and his allies.

Twenty-five years later, John Sims, ex-naval intelligence now head of chemistry, once again was faced with an intellectual challenge, albeit on a minor scale compared with his wartime experiences.

John's initial response was to set traps before he left at night, which he would check for evidence the following morning. He would arrange jars and bottles in particular patterns so that he could tell if they had been moved. When he was absolutely sure that a thief was at work he came to see me.

The only persons other than John who had access to his store were his cleaner and the head caretaker. Whilst it would have been foolish to completely dismiss them as suspects, it was very unlikely that a middle-aged lady or the keeper of the school would be silly enough to steal a pestle and mortar and a supply of chemicals.

"Have you any idea which particular chemicals are being stolen?" I enquired.

"Yes and that's what worries me," he replied. "In particular, I am concerned that a fair amount of potassium nitrate has gone and also some sulphur."

"Oh no!" I swallowed hard.

"Yes, some bright spark is playing with explosives. If he doesn't blow his own head off, he's likely to injure somebody else."

"And you say the stealing has been going on for about two weeks?" I hoped I was mistaken.

"As far as I can tell," said John, "it's difficult for me to pin-point when it started."

"Yes, I'm sure. Well, one thing is certain, we've got to find out whose pinching the stuff and what he's doing with it. Do you remember how we caught Alan Brown with that powder we got from Boots? You recommended it."

"Oh yes," John went on to pronounce the name of an unpronounceable substance which was brown when dry but which became bright green when in contact with liquid. The normal moisture on human skin was sufficient to change the colour and, what is more, the bright green pigment took several days to wear off, in spite of constant scrubbing.

We had first used the substance to catch a thief who was operating in the boys' cloakroom, particularly on Wednesday afternoons when the Fourth Year had their games lessons. A few coins were sprinkled with the powder and placed in the pocket of an unclaimed coat. Then, at fifteen minute intervals, a boy who was excused games was delegated to go along to the cloakroom and shake the coat. If the money no longer rattled he was to inform me.

On only his second foray his shaking was not answered by a jangle so my assistant detective was soon reporting to his chief. I immediately activated the bell to call a fire drill and within five minutes a host of boys and girls were lined up on the school field in their form groups. Among the fourth year pupils, shivering in their games kit, stood a boy with green hands and a face smeared with green streaks. I regretted that the whole school's lessons had been interrupted but I had considered the situation to be very serious and, therefore, a serious response had been called for. What is more, I was sure that the public exposure of Alan Brown was a salutary lesson to anyone else who may have contemplated petty pilfering.

The magic powder had been most effective on that occasion and now, several years later, we were once again confronted by a 'desperate disease' which required a 'desperate remedy'. That evening, John Sims and I contrived to work late until the caretaking and cleaning staff had completed their chores and left for home. We then dusted the inside knob of the store-room door with the brown powder and also deposited a small amount on the lid of the potassium nitrate jar. The door was carefully locked as was the outside door to the laboratory. Finally, I secured the main door to the school and we retired to the 'Rose and Crown' for a quick pint of the local brew.

Next morning we arrived simultaneously and very early, immediately proceeding to inspect the chemistry store. I'm not sure whether I was pleased or dismayed when John, unable to contain his excitement, gasped, "The bugger's been at it again!"

I retired to my study to think. Misgivings began to close in on me. What if the thief had realised where he picked up the green dye and had managed to obliterate it? Or if he had been unable to remove it, what if he had feigned illness or even played truant to allow the evidence to wear off? In either case, we should not have another chance to catch him and he would still have a quantity of chemicals which he had already stolen.

I need not have worried. Having asked the staff at my regular morning meeting to look out for any pupils with green stains on their hands, I proceeded to the assembly hall and stationed myself adjacent to the main entrance, nodding and smiling at the bright faces of my pupils as they filed past me. When poor Rupert came into view, I could not believe how conclusive a piece of evidence could be. He had a green stain on the left side of his forehead and, as he passed me, the green marks on his hands were clear for all to see.

There followed a remarkable train of events. As we sang the closing hymn of our morning worship, glancing over the heads of the girls and boys who sang lustily before me I saw, through the large window at the rear of the hall, a police panda car turn into the car-park. Two young officers in uniform were waiting for me when I returned to my study. One was clutching a yellow canvas hold-all.

"Come in gentlemen. What can I do for two intrepid guardians of the law?" In response, the contents of the yellow bag were emptied on to my coffee table. There were about a dozen envelopes of various sizes, some white but most were brown. All were charred: many almost completely destroyed.

"Some nutter put a firework into the letter box at the end of the road," began the smaller of the two officers.

"Do you normally post your letters after the 5p.m. collection?" asked his colleague.

"Almost never," I replied, "but last night I worked late and I had not signed the post when my secretary left so I offered to drop them into the box myself."

"Can you be specific with regard to when you posted them?"

"Yes, as a matter of fact, I can. It would be sometime after six thirty but before six fifty."

"How can you be so precise?"

"Because, having dropped them in the box, I walked to the 'Rose and Crown' and 'The Archers' signature tune was just beginning on the bar radio. It takes about fifteen minutes to stroll from school to the pub."

"Hm, well this may be very helpful. Thanks. It's fortunate that you're definite about the times because there's no-one else to ask. Apart from a post card that was charred beyond recognition, there was no other mail in the box but yours. The firework must have been dropped in soon after you posted your letters."

The other officer chimed in, "Well, sorry about it, we'll do our best to find out who's responsible."

They left me wondering. After a while I sent for Rupert. My day had started with a vengeance.

"Sit down, Rupert."

"Thank you, Sir."

"Rupert, were you on the premises after school last night?"

"The premises, Sir? Do you mean the grounds or the buildings?"

He was hedging. The green dye on his hands proved it was he who had been in the chemistry store but how had he managed it?

"You know perfectly well what I mean."

"Well yes, I did come back to school last night. I'd forgotten a book I needed for my homework. It was all locked up."

"Then how did you get your book?"

He pondered. "I climbed through a window. I'm very sorry. It was wrong of me to do it."

"Show me which window you climbed through."

"Which window, Sir? How do you mean?"

"I mean which window did you climb through? Some of the windows are alarmed."

He pondered again. "I didn't climb in through a window. I came through the side door. It wasn't locked."

"You're telling lies Rupert. I locked that door myself. Get your coat: we are going home to see your parents." Rupert's mother kept a haberdashery shop, occasionally assisted by his father, who was a part-time insurance agent.

They were partaking of morning coffee when we arrived. I came straight to the point regarding my suspicions about the chemicals. Neither parent took kindly to my accusations but father took the initiative. "We'll soon settle this. You can come up with me into the loft where Rupert keeps all his tackle. He's been up there quite a lot lately."

87

"No Dad, there's nothing up there," pleaded the boy.

"Let's have a look." I felt we were getting warm and this was soon confirmed. The loft was a typical hideaway for a teenager: sky-light, small table doubling as a desk with an angle-poise lamp and a few book-shelves. However, it was the old-fashioned marble-topped wash-stand which caught my attention or, at least, the bottles of chemicals arranged like soldiers in a line on top of it. In the cupboard below I found a pestle and mortar together with several glass flasks and an assortment of zinc spoons. The boy, the father and the headmaster were all devastated for different reasons.

"What can I say?" was how Rupert's father broke the long silence which had lasted until we had descended the retractable ladder and seated ourselves in the living room.

"It's not your fault. You had no reason to suspect what Rupert was up to." I tried to lessen the shock both parents must have been feeling.

"I wouldn't be too sure about that!" Mother spoke for the first time. In answer to my quizzical frown, Father explained, "My wife is referring to my interest in war games."

"You talk of nothing else to the boy." She moved towards the door. "I must get back to the shop." Then, over her shoulder, "And then there's all those survival weekends you've taken him on. His mind must be full of maps and guns." She was gone and I was left alone with Father, Rupert having been banished to his room.

The man was clearly uncomfortable. I sensed that he wanted to talk so I remained in my seat and fixed him with a look that enquired "Where do we go from here?"

He lit a cigarette, offered his pack to me, which I declined, and then he followed up with, "Mind if I do?" He started to fill in the details of the pursuit he enjoyed with Rupert, obviously to his wife's disapproval. I soon realised why she was unhappy.

It all emanated from the man's fascination with war, weapons, strategies, resistance movements and matters relating. As his story developed, the significance of his personal appearance became apparent. He was on the small side but he compensated for this by holding his head high and his shoulders back. He sported a military moustache and wore highly polished black shoes and an olive green jersey with leather patches on the shoulders and on the sleeves. He spoke with awesome respect about exploits of individuals in war situations. Clearly he experienced a vicarious thrill from his hobby and he left me in no doubt that he was largely responsible for his son's obsession with explosives.

My instinct was to avoid making a hasty decision about which I may repent at leisure so I asked him to keep Rupert at home that day and bring him in to see me on the morrow. Meanwhile, Mr Sims and I would work out the full extent of what was missing from his store.

As I drove back to school I thought about Rupert, the quiet lad who was adept at fishing, camping and learning fast the art of manufacturing explosives. With boys like him on our side, no wonder we defeated Napoleon and the Third Reich. Even so, I did not anticipate what would surface next morning.

Father and son arrived when assembly, taken by Paul Robson, my deputy, was in full swing. As I walked down the short passage to the entrance hall to greet my two visitors the whole building began to reverberate with the sound of the fire alarm, which mercifully ceased ringing as abruptly as it had started.

The scene I came upon was bizarre. Rupert and his father were struggling and crunching broken glass under their feet. My secretary stood watching them. She was white with anger.

"That idiot has just smashed the glass on the fire alarm. If I hadn't been near the governing switch, anything could have happened." At that moment, two young teachers emerged from the assembly hall presumably to investigate. "It's OK. Ask Mr Robson to continue, please." I took control. "Thank you, Mrs Jones and well done. Please get someone to sweep up the glass." The wrestling had ceased and Father had Rupert in some kind of judo hold. "Bring him to my study, please."

I placed myself between Rupert and the door and we all sat down. "What on earth possessed you to do that?" I began.

"Mr Firestone will think you're a nutter," added his father. We both glared at the wide-eyed boy who did look a little crazy.

"The panic! I wanted to see them all come tumbling out of the hall, falling on top of each other." He was mad! His father's use of the word 'nutter' rang a bell but my attention was immediately diverted when the embarrassed fellow placed a bunch of keys on my table. "I found these in one of his drawers."

I gazed at this new discovery for several seconds, then I looked enquiringly at the boy. He grinned sheepishly. "Where on earth did you get all these?" It was my turn to feel embarrassed. "It was easy," he paused, then added, "Sir." I wanted to wipe the smirk from his face. Instead I said, "Tell me."

"Right. A couple of weeks ago I told that new lady cleaner that I'd left my satchel in our form room. I guessed that she would refuse to go all the way upstairs with me and I was right. She lent me a key, told me not to lose it as it was the only one she had. 'A skeleton', I thought. I ran to the sheds, jumped on my bike and belted it into the village, had a duplicate cut at the ironmonger's and belted it back. She played hell with me for being such a long time but I told her I'd had trouble finding my bag. I think she believed me."

I looked at his father but he averted his eyes. "That doesn't explain where you got the others."

"Ah well, that was even easier. I used the skeleton to get into school one Saturday afternoon, found the caretaker's bunch of keys and had duplicates of them all cut in the village."

"And that's how you got the chemicals?" I wondered if he would join the SAS or become a bank robber. What do 'nutters' do when they grow up? I don't know about a 'nutter', he was a bloody genius. The word 'nutter' reminded me of the policeman's words: "A nutter put a firework in the post box."

I leaned forward. "If you are so clever, Mr Rupert, why did you set fire to a letter box so near to the school?" I was guessing; hoping that his vanity would be his undoing. He took the bait.

"I didn't just want to set fire to it. I wanted it to explode into pieces: you know, fly all over."

"My God!" Father exhaled through pursed lips.

"Yes indeed," said I. "I'm very sorry but I am bound to contact the police. They have already been to see me about the burnt letters. In any case, it won't take their forensic guys long to discover that chemicals were used to cause the fire."

I don't think anyone spoke for several minutes. I broke the silence. "Well, you can say goodbye to the keys."

"Bye, bye, keys." Rupert pointed the palm of his right hand towards them, then closed and opened his fingers several times in a subdued wave which matched his rueful smile.

He completed his education in a residential school for maladjusted children. His parents sold their business and moved to another town so I have no idea either how he developed or what line of activity he is now engaged in. He was an able boy with great powers of initiative. I hope that the early discovery and exposure of his deviant tendencies enabled him to assess his personal situation and so encourage him to apply his talents to worthy pursuits.

If that, indeed, has been the outcome, then the time and effort spent in catching him early was worth-while.

CHAPTER 11

"TURNING THE TABLES"

"Justice should not only be done, but manifestly and undoubtedly be seen to be done."

LORD HEWART 1870-1943

This is a tale of two teenage boys who shared the same shrewd lawyer. The fact that, at their time of life, it had been necessary for them to seek legal advice might lead one to conclude that their social behaviour was below standard. One would be quite correct to reach such a conclusion.

Neither of them had been born, bred and nurtured at Lea Grange in that they had joined the school mid-way through their secondary careers. Thus they had been deprived of the valuable initiation period enjoyed by all first year entrants when they are constantly reminded by me of their good fortune in joining such a wonderful school and of the responsibilities that such a privilege places upon their young shoulders. Perhaps, of even more importance, they had not received the advice and warning which the older pupils traditionally pass on to new first year boys and girls: "If you get up to mischief, it's better to own up straight away, for he'll not rest until he finds you out," or words to that effect.

By slipping into Lea Grange at the third year stage, almost unnoticed, they had missed an essential component of their education and development.

Brian was the first to join us, introduced through Tom, our Head of Religious Studies. The family was experiencing a very depressing period and, in his goodness, Tom suggested the move to Lea Grange as a first step to improving matters.

Both he and Brian's mother attended the same evangelical church, which was noted for its strong pastoral traditions. A few months earlier, Tom had observed a deterioration in the good lady's general demeanour and, by skilful probing, had learned from her 'in the strictest confidence' that her husband had been committed to prison. The tax authorities, two banks and his accountant were all involved but the net result was that he had been found guilty of embezzlement and duly incarcerated. Almost immediately Brian's standard of behaviour plummeted and he was soon instructing his father's lawyer to represent him on a charge of shop-lifting. Having been caught red-handed, he had pleaded guilty and received a period of probation.

About that time, someone in his previous school had learned of the family misdemeanours and Brian was soon suffering jibes: 'like father, like son,' or 'following in dad's footsteps' or even 'watch your pockets, here comes a thief'. Thus Tom, who by now was almost permanently counselling Brian's mother, offered to seek my help in obtaining a transfer of schools.

I regret to say that, if his father was indeed a swindler, Brian was quick to reveal similar tendencies. Soon after he joined us, Christmas approached and he, like all the other boys and girls, was issued with a book of ten raffle tickets and urged to sell them in aid of our chosen charity.

The first hint of trouble came through a telephone message from the warden of an old people's block of flats. A young boy had called and invited an old gentleman to buy a raffle ticket. As the old fellow had no coinage, the boy had offered to change his five pound note at the corner shop, an errand from which he had not returned.

The boy had left the raffle ticket at the flat and it was printed with the Lea Grange name and logo, enabling the warden to trace its origins. Our school welfare officer was promptly dispatched to offer our apologies, reimburse the pensioner and recover the ticket. Its serial number indicated that it had been issued to a pupil in Form 3B and, as the tutor had recorded the serial numbers with the names of the recipients, we did not need Sherlock Holmes to tell us who had attempted to cheat the old man.

When confronted with this irrefutable evidence, together with the fact that the flats were several miles from the school but in the neighbourhood where he lived, Brian's initial reaction was still to deny all knowledge of the matter. However, when informed that he and I were to visit the old man to proffer a personal apology, he bowed to the inevitable and expressed his tearful regret, then rather too swiftly asked if it would be necessary to involve the police. He had already realised the dire consequences of committing an offence whilst on probation.

That afternoon, promptly at two o'clock, I was ushered into the warden's office, a sea of red and grey: grey walls; grey desk; two grey filing cabinets; grey chairs with red plastic seats and red curtains with grey stripes.

The occupant was a fierce looking lady in late middle age, grey hair swept back into a bun. She wore a dark green trouser suit with buttoned epaulettes and a watch clipped to her left lapel. Clearly she would be a force to be reckoned with in any situation. There were no pleasantries, no prevarication: she had advised Mr Gibson to let her report the disgraceful matter to the police. She was tired of the number of thefts and acts of vandalism around the flats. The youth of today needed much firmer handling by parents and teachers , and so on.

She fell short of labelling me as a latter-day Fagin but Brian was certainly an artful dodger and he deserved to be punished. I was about to echo her sentiments and to remind her of the swift action the school had already taken to resolve the matter when the old gentleman was brought to the office by a strapping young lady who wore a dark red overall. I deliberately use the verb 'brought' rather than 'escorted' and the adjective 'strapping' because the frail old man needed real support just to progress from the threshold across the room and into a chair.

Now I understood the warden's anger and hostility. The thought of one of my pupils cheating this poor old fellow filled me with shame. My expressions of sorrow and apology, although completely sincere, seemed totally inadequate as Mr Gibson half raised his hand to restrain me.

"Please don't trouble yourself, Sir. Let's give the lad a chance to speak up for himself."

A sobbing Brian, with bowed head, poured out the saga of the recent months of his life, one misfortune following another in a steady flow. The warden was clearly unmoved. My feelings were a mixture of anger towards him and sympathy for him. He had obviously received more than his share of ill fortune.

It was the old pensioner's reaction which took us all by surprise. With tears welling in his clear blue eyes he slowly rose to his feet and held out his unsteady arms to Brian. The boy's face was soon buried against the old man's cardigan as he clung to him for dear life. They could have been grandfather and grandson.

The warden was as embarrassed as I was. I think we both attempted to speak: neither could decide what to say. After an eternity, during which I had undertaken a painstaking examination of my shoes and brushed several imaginary threads from my trousers, she proclaimed, "I'm going to send for a pot of tea." Obviously, this was a well tried, successful remedy for such occasions.

Something certainly worked a minor miracle on Brian's behalf for the proposition to involve the police was rejected, and incredibly the decision was unanimous. It was Mr Gibson who won us over.

In his youth, he had been in trouble several times and he was sure that, without the help of understanding adults, he would have become an habitual offender. He offered to give Brian a similar chance. He hoped they could keep in touch and he would like to be informed of the lad's progress from time to time. In the discussion that ensued a wonderful arrangement was worked out: Brian would call on Mr Gibson on his way home from school every Friday and do any small jobs that were needed. This agreement would be monitored by the warden and Brian's form tutor.

The arrangement proved to be very successful and was still in operation when the incident concerning our other late entrant occurred. Gary was fourteen and he lived within our catchment area. A clever boy, he had won a scholarship to an independent day school where, according to his Headmaster 'he had never really settled down'. I soon realised that this description of Gary's situation was, at the best, euphemistic and, at the worst, grossly misleading.

The initial application for admission was submitted by his mother on the advice of his present Headmaster. Apparently, he was finding the work at a selective school too difficult and, as his elder brother had done well at Lea Grange, she felt that a transfer would be good for Gary. He had been giving her quite a bit of trouble since his father had left to live with a younger woman about two years earlier.

At interview, Gary presented himself well. He was a big lad for his age, keen on sport, alert and knowledgeable. He was eager to join the school at which his brother had been so successful and, like his mother, he urged us to give him the chance to prove himself.

The interview took place in July. By the time he joined us in September we had already received a request for a court welfare report: he had brutally assaulted a younger boy in a local playing field during the summer break. As Gary was comparatively unknown to me, I redirected the request to his previous school. It was only when I received my copy of his ex-Headmaster's report that I realised that Gary's propensity for trouble had been flagrantly under-stated.

During the following twelve months, Paul Robson, my Deputy, spent an inordinate amount of time on Gary: counselling; encouraging; supporting; admonishing; and, ultimately, punishing. The lad was always causing trouble both in class and outside the form room. I was particularly concerned about the likely effect of his behaviour on his fellow students. In addition to disturbing their concentration and retarding their progress, he began to recruit a small number of followers from among our less-motivated brethren.

We had acquired further confirmation of his previous poor record soon after his arrival when he 'threatened' Paul Robson with his social worker. Although it is dangerous to generalise, the existence of a social worker attached to a family usually suggests a deficiency of some kind: in this case the reason was quite clear: Gary was completely out of control at home. The earnest young man was utterly dedicated to his work and very agreeable to deal with. If he had a fault, it was his myopic belief in Gary and a refusal to acknowledge that the boy himself was at least partially responsible for the problems which constantly plagued him. Thus he became a permanent spokesman on Gary's behalf, always ready with an excuse for bad behaviour. In the long run, this became counter-productive to the boy's moral development.

The shrewd lawyer entered the frame as a result of Gary's being caught in possession of a firearm one Sunday evening. Although it was only a small air pistol, he was committing an offence and he was duly charged and summoned to appear in the juvenile court. On his previous appearance he had received a warning so he was likely to be dealt with more severely this time. Our report on him was frank, truthful and therefore not helpful to his lawyer's pleas for mitigation. However, bureaucratic carelessness on our part presented the astute advocate with a golden opportunity to gain sympathy for his young client. Our clerical staff had failed to fill in the boxes which were intended to show recent attendance. As Gary's record was very good, the lawyer made a great fuss in court and suggested that the school was deliberately withholding facts that would be helpful to the boy. The outcome was that Gary was placed on probation and we were placed on the alert with regard to that particular gentleman of the law.

Three weeks later, Gary and I were once again face to face. A new humanities area had been added to our buildings and it contained its own clean and airy toilet block; facilities which would have graced any modern hospital. Thus I was indescribably angry as I surveyed the damage which had been reported to me before 10 a.m. one morning. Two white wooden division panels had been smashed from their fittings by someone who had prised them apart using the soles of his shoes as a battering ram. A quickly coordinated check round the form rooms revealed that only three boys had received permission to visit the toilet. Gary was one of them. An elementary forensic examination matched the marks on the shattered panels with the soles of Gary's shoes and, within an hour his social worker, whose immediate presence I had demanded, shared my dismay, if not anger.

"What do you intend to do about it, Headmaster?"

"It's wanton, criminal damage. He will have to be reported."

"But the police, they'll lock him up," he stammered.

"That's no more than he deserves," I responded. "One thing's certain: he can't continue here."

"Headmaster, will you grant me twenty-four hours to find him a 'secure' place. I'll ensure that he remains there until the end of his schooling. He's only got eight months to go. It will save him adding to his police record."

"Take him with you. I don't want to see him again. If you don't confirm his 'secure' placement by tomorrow morning, I shall report the matter to the police,"

After Gary's departure, life resumed a much more normal pattern. I wished we could have done more to help him but he was an unusually difficult individual. Heaven knows what problems he would have caused if we hadn't stopped him at a fairly early stage.

Then, one afternoon, a few weeks before he was due to be released, Gary absconded from his 'secure' placement and returned to Lea Grange. He waited outside the gates until the pupils were dismissed whereupon he brutally assaulted Brian, our other anti-hero, with whom he had a long standing vendetta, then promptly disappeared.

Paul Robson ran Brian home and explained the situation to his mother who insisted on dealing with the matter herself. She specifically requested that we should take no action.

The following day I received a 'phone call from our legal friend.

"Hello, Headmaster. I'm sorry to be the harbinger of bad news but I've been instructed to register a complaint against you," was how he began.

"Well let's hear it!"

"Last evening, a young boy, who is a client of mine, was severely assaulted by a pupil of yours as he left the premises. Clearly, there was a lack of staff supervision and we intend to institute proceedings against you. We are seeking compensation."

Although I was seething with rage, I spoke calmly into the receiver. I was glad that we were not face to face.

"May I say that I share your concern and I will do all I can to assist you with your action. In fact, the aggressor is not a pupil of ours but I do happen to know his name and address."

I sensed the lawyer was listening intently but he made no effort to speak. I continued, "Actually, I believe you know him. Yes, I remember now. You have represented him in the past. He may still be one of your clients. What a remarkable coincidence! Yes, his name is Gary, you know, the boy with the air pistol. Are you still there?"

"Er, yes, Gary? You mean the very clever boy?"

"That's him." I tried not to sound triumphant. "Are you going to begin your civil proceedings by obtaining a criminal conviction?"

I thought at first that we had been cut off but a reply was eventually forthcoming. "Look, I'd like to think about this. Will you leave it with me and I'll be back in touch."

I am still waiting to hear from him. No doubt with such a conflict of interest he is having difficulty in balancing the scales of justice.

CHAPTER 12

"THE BLACK HAND GANG"

"How often have I said to you that when you have eliminated the impossible, whatever remains, however improbable, must be the truth?"

SHERLOCK HOLMES: "THE SIGN OF FOUR"
SIR ARTHUR CONAN DOYLE 1859-1930

The Black Hand Gang's reign of terror ended as abruptly as it began. At least, that was what everyone thought. I knew otherwise. I knew the whole story from beginning to end, particularly the end, and I was not likely to broadcast it.

The saga lasted for about six months during which time the gang achieved a considerable degree of notoriety in Beckbridge. Their activities suggested that they were a group of young boys rather than a band of hardened criminals. Indeed, until their final act, which brought about their downfall, they regularly committed the offence of illegally entering non-residential premises without doing anything more than leaving their trade-mark to provide proof of their visit.

The fact that they broke into such places as solicitors' offices and accountants' as well as grocery stores and hardware shops caused a great deal of consternation among the local populace and, indirectly, a considerable amount of embarrassment to me. No weekly meeting of the Rotary Club passed without some reference to the Black Hand Gang. Far too frequently, members reported that their premises had received nocturnal visits and they produced the Gang's calling card to prove it: a black hand imprinted on a piece of white paper; the identical type we used in our art department. The similarity was not lost on my Rotarian friends.

"The little devils are obviously from your school. Can't you control them Adam?" The grocer.

"Control them! I know what I shall do to them if I catch them in my place." The tobacconist, who had so far been spared.

"Nobody knows who they are and where they are from," was my usual way of defending the name of Lea Grange. I would then add, "We don't even know how old they are. I'm sure that my students have outgrown such childish mischief."

But I was uneasy and events proved that I had good reason to be. In due course, I was to discover that the gang was made up of four boys and two girls, all pupils at my school. The oldest was thirteen and the youngest eleven. The events leading up to their exposure, which, to my relief, was unknown to all save myself and ultimately the vicar, had more than a touch of fatalism about them.

It all arose out of my firm belief that any school with strong traditions in music and sport is likely to be a good school. Accordingly, to further the development of music at Lea Grange, we had decided to form a brass band. Our initial target was to raise enough money to purchase twelve large instruments such as basses, trombones and euphoniums. We knew that interested parents would be prepared to buy cornets and trumpets but we could not expect them to spend the greater amounts of money required to purchase the larger instruments.

We were determined to raise all the required cash in one mighty swoop. We would organise a large garden fete in our picturesque grounds. At the time we took the decision, we set in motion a bizarre train of events which eventually led to the detection of the Black Hand Gang.

It is relevant that, during the period we were establishing our music, the school was undergoing a large-scale building development and there was a continuous presence of workmen and their equipment. Rather than allow this to be a disadvantage, we examined ways of deriving benefit from our situation. An unlimited amount of sand enabled us to establish a play-pit, for which we could charge an entry fee, and there was no shortage of planks and loose bricks at our disposal. With these materials we constructed several stalls, a coconut shy and, with the help of two carpenters, an intricate ducking stool.

To compensate for our having to relinquish four class-rooms for building renovations we were supplied with two double mobile hutments, which were positioned on the perimeter of the games field. They were delivered during the week prior to the big day so we stored their desks in the main school and utilised one building as a bingo hall and the other for ticket sales and other administration.

A local goalkeeping celebrity, who was related to one of our physical education staff, was booked to open the fete and, later, to pit his skill against would-be scorers of penalty kicks, charging for each attempt, of course. Finally, a staff-meeting devoted exclusively to the garden-f,te was held to ensure that we all were clear about our individual duties. One suggestion from a member of staff, who had previous experience of such fund-raising activities, still causes me to smile: in all events where water is involved, any prize money should be given in the form of wet coins. Invariably, rather than put the wet coils into pockets or purses, recipients would try their luck again. It was inevitable that the coins would end up in our coffers.

The Saturday of the fete was a lovely sunny day. The event was duly declared open promptly at two-o-clock by a giant of a man who looked capable of filling the space between two goal-posts just by his physical bulk. Thankfully, my fears that nobody would be foolish enough to spend money trying to score against him proved to be groundless.

Droves of people poured through the gates dropping their entrance money into builders' buckets, which had been scraped clean of sand and cement. Music blasted out from impromptu systems of loud-speakers and the aroma of hot-dogs and beef-burgers permeated the air space around the stalls. I was indulging myself in the veritable carnival atmosphere when the first crisis struck. A concerned young lady teacher breathlessly informed me that a Mrs Roebuck had collapsed and was lying down in the medical room.

My anxiety for the welfare of a fellow human being overcame my reluctance to leave the position I had taken up outside the erstwhile bingo hall, where I was fascinated to hear Bernie Lord, our Year Three Head, calling the numbers. "All the threes, thirty three, legs eleven, two fat ladies." I wondered if, like competence at snooker, a sound knowledge of bingo slang betrayed a misspent youth.

Mrs Roebuck had been persuaded to sit up and drink a cup of tea but my arrival brought about a minor relapse in her condition.

"Mr Firestone, how could you?" I needed a few facts before I could begin to answer.

"Now you must not upset yourself, Mrs Roebuck," I began. Then I added, "How could I do what?"

"My father would turn in his grave." She raised both arms, then bent almost double. "Oh no, no, no!"

"Mrs Roebuck, you will have to explain yourself a little if you want me to help."

"The piano, my father's piano! They're going to smash it to pieces!" The uncontrollable sobbing resumed.

I racked my brains. The piano, her father's piano, the piano bashing contest. "How fortunate we are that you noticed. A dreadful mistake has been made. I'll sort it out at once." With that I left Mrs Roebuck in the capable hands of two young teachers and rushed to the area set aside for the three cornered piano breaking contest: pupils versus staff versus parents.

Roger Hansard, our Head of Music, was just unloading six sledge hammers from a wheel-barrow, all items courtesy of the builders.

"How the hell has Mrs Roebuck's piano got mixed up with this lot?" was my unambiguous request. Roger was his usual supercilious self. "Because I put it there. It's useless: the stops are all shot."

"Meaning what?"

"Meaning that it cannot be tuned. When we tried to tune it, all the stops slipped. It's long past its sell-by date."

"That may be so but when Mrs Roebuck donated it she thought it was for the second music room, not to be hammered to bits. It was her dad's."

"More likely her great granddad's!"

In fact, the problem was sorted out very quickly. Roger had two more old pianos on the corridor outside his music department. Prior to the fete, he had appealed for old pianos for the bashing contest and he had obtained four. Two stood on the field next to Mrs Roebuck's but, as the other two were in quite good condition, he had decided to preserve them and use hers. The switch back was made before the hammers struck and Mrs Roebuck was duly mollified.

By then, events were in full swing and the first batch of sponsored balloons was being released into the atmosphere. One hundred red, white or blue balloons, each decorated with a transfer of the face of a pop star and filled with helium, rose into the sky and floated off in an easterly direction. To each one was attached a ticket bearing the name of the purchaser together with a printed request. Whoever found the balloon was asked to return the ticket to the school address. The finder of the ticket that had travelled the furthest would receive a prize and so would the original purchaser. In fact, the winning balloon was found in Germany.

There was an amusing spin off to this competition in that John Sims, our Chemistry Head, who was in charge of the helium process, decided to play a trick on Bernie Lord. Whilst Bernie was busily engaged on his bingo calling duties, John removed the ticket which bore Bernie's name. Two weeks later, the school closed for the summer holiday and John took Bernie's ticket with him on his vacation to Canada. Of course, when the ticket arrived back at school, duly soiled for effect, bearing a Canadian stamp, it appeared to be the winner. When it was pointed out that all the balloons had left in an easterly direction, Bernie was quick to claim that his balloon must have circumnavigated the globe. Eventually we decided enough was enough and we told him the disappointing truth.

The balloons contributed greatly to the festive atmosphere. Not only were clouds of them released skywards at regular intervals but some parents bought bunches for their children to clutch like bouquets of outsize blooms. Indeed it was the Black Hand Gang's involvement with balloons that eventually led to its downfall but this did not happen until two days later. However, although I was not aware of it at the time, two of its members were responsible for the next problem which occurred, less than an hour after the piano breaking fiasco had been dealt with. Two little girls drew my attention to a jet of water that was spouting majestically upwards from somewhere behind the gym and reaching a height of about fifty feet. They also gave me the names of two boys whom they had witnessed fooling about in that area just prior to the start of the deluge.

The scene at the source of the jet was like a Laurel and Hardy film. Bill Brown, the school keeper, and Denis, the groundsman were trying to stem the unstoppable flow which was spurting from a high-pressure plastic hose-pipe. The builders were using this pipe as an emergency supply whilst they installed new permanent pipes. Both men were soaked to the skin as they managed to manoeuvre an upturned piece of cast-iron guttering to cover the jet, which then spurted sideways. Several rocks were used to keep the gutter pipe in place before Bill spoke. He nodded towards a pick-axe.

"Some idiot has spiked the main water supply! I can't turn it off because of the toilets."

"You've done well. We'll get it repaired over the week-end," I replied. "Get into some dry clothes. I'm going to look for two very wet little boys!"

I soon found them but they had already out-smarted me. They had volunteered to help with the ducking stool apparently behaving recklessly when replacing the plastic buckets. The master in charge and several onlookers were still laughing at the way the two lads had managed to spill so much water on themselves: an unshakeable alibi.

"I'll see you two in my study at morning break on Monday. I shall want a very good explanation as to how you have got so wet." In fact, by the time I met them, there was much more to discuss.

The remaining hours passed without further embarrassment and I arrived home with the knowledge that we had achieved our financial target. At ten o'clock the telephone rang. It was the vicar. Would I please meet him straight away at the church. It was essential that I should go immediately.

Without a word, he beckoned me to follow him into the vestry and down a flight of rickety steps into the vault beneath the church. When my eyes became accustomed to the dim light afforded by a low wattage bulb, my first impression was of several ghostly figures dancing on the tables. A closer examination revealed a number of white balloons, my balloons, attached to three or four tables by lengths of string, waving in the draught from the iron grills at both ends of the vault.

Several folding chairs were positioned round a central table on top of which stood two candles and a box of matches. Beside them, under a large pebble which acted as a paper weight, I was horrified to find a pile of art paper torn into pieces the size of large postcards. Each piece had the same design stencilled on it: a black hand.

"Peter, how did you find all this?" He nodded towards a table by one of the grills. "Those two balloons were visible against the grill. I nearly fainted when I walked past on my way home. I really thought that I was seeing a couple of ghosts. We've already had two funerals this week!"

Self preservation took charge. "Have you told anyone else about this?"

"Only you, Adam." His reply was exactly what I prayed it would be. Of course, the black hand pamphlets had led him to me and I was thankful that he had met no-one on the way. He agreed to my two requests: to leave any action to my discretion and to tell nobody.

"We've got to catch these beggars before anyone else beats us to it."

Peter, the vicar, assured me that I could count on his full co-operation as well as his silence and we sat formulating a plan of action. I was so thankful that my friendship with him extended back over twenty years to the Saturday afternoons when we had regularly kicked the stuffing out of each other whilst playing for opposite sides in the High Peak Football League. I knew that I could rely on him. We rejected the idea of installing Peter's baby alarm and eventually returned to the first plan we thought of: Peter would spend the next three nights in the vestry, quietly contemplating next Sunday's sermon.

We spoke briefly after evensong the following day, which was Sunday, of course. I wished him luck and I walked home via the school field. My youngest son met me at our gate. "The vicar has just 'phoned. He wants you to go back to church. What's going on Dad?"

Disregarding his question, I returned by the shortest route and I was soon under the postern gate receiving my henchman's whispered account. Our quarry were in place in the vault. Hastily, we agreed that Peter would return to the vestry and noisily unlock the door leading to the vault, whilst I would wait outside the grill to catch the gang as they fled.

The operation was a complete success. Four dejected boys, including the two I had met at the ducking stool, and two innocent looking girls stood before me. Sadly, they were all known to me. Thankfully, they had been tracked down by me rather than by some angry shop-keeper.

The important factor was that the Black Hand Gang ceased to exist and I was determined that it should not be re-incarnated. I was equally determined that its members' identities would not leak out and bring discredit upon the school. With this uppermost in my mind I formally summoned their parents to meet me in school the following evening. They ranged from an angry bus driver, resplendent in his oatmeal jacket with his round H.G.V. badge on the lapel, to several serious looking fathers in grey suits and a tearfully grateful widow. The bus driver was angry with me for causing him to miss part of his work schedule but he soon joined the rest in venting his ire on the children when he, like the other parents, learned the full extent of their little darlings' exploits. I was only too pleased to accept their sincere undertakings to be far more watchful with regard to how their sons and daughters spent their future leisure and, accordingly, the memory of the Black Hand Gang was, that day, forever laid to rest.

CHAPTER 13

"THE BISHOP'S CANDLESTICKS"

"So long as the three problems of the age - the degradation of man by poverty, the ruin of women by starvation, and the dwarfing of childhood by physical and spiritual right - are not solved; ...... books like this cannot be useless."
Extract from the author's preface to "Les Miserables."

VICTOR MARIE HUGO, 1802 - 1885

The disruption caused by holding a garden fete on school premises during term time has to be experienced to be believed so I was enormously relieved when our routine was back to normal. In particular, I felt so much better when we stopped using the mobile class rooms as ticket offices and bingo halls.

Whether or not the school's misuse of the huts for the garden fete had set the wrong example and encouraged Alan McNab, alias Monkey, to treat them disrespectfully I shall never know. The plain fact is that, on only the second day of their proper use, he inflicted considerable damage to the interior wall panels of his designated form room.

When the vandalism was first reported to me, we had no idea who was responsible. The initial break-through, which resulted in the exposure of Monkey McNab as the culprit, was made by Paul Robson, the Deputy Headmaster. His success was based on a theory I had formulated many years earlier : the fact that evil-doers often stay away on the day after their crime.

That particular discovery is almost a story in itself. The cycle of events leading up to it began as early as my second day at Lea Grange. On that fateful day, shortly after the commencement of the lunch break, I was disturbed by a hesitant knock at my door. A very small boy stood nervously on the threshold.

"Please Sir, two big boys are smoking in the junior toilets."

"Are they, by Jove! Well, don't you worry about it. Off you go to lunch and leave it to me."

The illicit smokers had chosen their hideaway with considerable skill, no doubt with the benefit of long experience, because the junior toilets were situated at the end of a long corridor at the opposite side of the building to the dining hall. As I stepped out of my study, a quick glance along the corridor revealed a lone body lurking outside the said toilets, obviously acting as look-out.

I strode purposefully in the opposite direction along the corridor and I soon entered the dining hall. Once inside, instead of taking a seat, I walked straight through and out of the door at the far end. I was then able to leave the premises, skirt round the perimeter of the school and re-enter our grounds by a wicket gate adjacent to the junior toilets.

My sudden appearance from an unexpected direction petrified the guard and I was soon facing two astounded youths in the smoke-filled lavatory area, the cause of the pollution literally in their own hands.

"Gentlemen, when you have completed your ablutions, I should like you to join me in my study."

I was soon responding to their knock.

"Come in."

"Sir, before you take any action, will you allow me to make a short statement?"

"Go ahead."

"Well Sir, Richard and I wish to extend to you our most sincere congratulations on your success in catching us smoking." James Tiler was the speaker. He went on, "Richard and I have been at this school for almost five years and I think it's true to say that we have smoked on practically every day without ever being caught. Obviously, you will punish us. We deserve it but, before you do, we both want you to know how we admire the way you caught us on only your second day here." Whilst James spoke, Richard nodded at appropriate intervals.

110

"Have you finished?"

Richard spoke, "Yes Sir, except to assure you how deeply sorry we are for causing you inconvenience and to assure you that we shall never smoke again in school.

I couldn't help comparing these smooth-talking sophisticated cads with the blatant rogues I had been used to in my previous school.

"Does that go for you too?" I nodded towards James

"Yes sir. I solemnly swear that I'll never smoke again on school premises."

I restrained an impulse to smile. Instead, I regarded them both with an even gaze and allowed the silence to intensify their obvious discomfort.

"Right, I'll accept your solemn and serious undertaking. I won't frighten you by telling you what will happen if you let me down. You may go."

Several days later, I looked in on a rehearsal for a gymnastics display and I was astonished to find that the star turn was James Tiler. He was chosen to round off every demonstration by performing a more difficult exercise than his team mates. If they executed a single somersault, James would respond with a double. If five sections of the vaulting box were cleared by the main group, a sixth would be added for James.

In similar circumstances, I discovered that Richard Hunter, James's fellow smoking culprit, was a prominent member of the lacrosse team. Inevitably, by attending displays and supporting the school's fixtures, I came to know both boys fairly well. Of even more importance, through James and Richard, I quickly widened my circle of acquaintances among the other pupils, a development which I welcomed for many reasons. In the first place, I am very fond of kids and I really enjoy their company but there was an additional spin off. The pupils were able to get to know me, to realise that I am human, that I treat people fairly and that I have no time for elitism or favouritism. It is in such ways that the right type of atmosphere in a school is created and I was soon to feel the benefit of the pupil co-operation that had been engendered so early in my headship.

In my capacity as a "new broom" I was tightening up in some areas and, sadly, the pupil co-operation was not one hundred per-cent. The most annoying protest was the smashing of a wall mirror in the senior cloakroom, particularly worrying because news of the dastardly act would soon be relayed round the school. What would be next?

Swift detection and summary justice were essential if my attempts to establish an orderly atmosphere were not to suffer a severe set-back. In fact, James Tiler provided the clue I so desperately needed.

"If I'd done something like that I wouldn't dare set foot in the school again : not for a long time, at least!"

I have often wondered whether this was an innocent observation or whether he was deliberately pointing me in the direction of the culprit. What I did do was to order a check of the attendance registers. This provided me with a list of absentees, which was quickly pruned into an even shorter list of suspects.

The matter was quickly resolved. The boy's father paid for the damage and promised to deduct the cost from his son's weekly allowance. I know that the school was impressed by the speed and success of the operation. Any thoughts of copying such conduct were laid to rest. Incidentally, the mirror basher is now in his mid-thirties and he is "mine host" at a rural pub on the outskirts of Bolton. I trust he has installed stainless steel mirrors in his gents' toilets.

To return to the saga of Monkey McNab, it was his absence from school that led Paul Robson to suspect his involvement in the damage to the walls of the form room. Monkey had been admitted to Lea Grange about a year before the incident. He was fourteen years of age and he had just been discharged from hospital after breaking his leg, an injury which he had brought upon himself through engaging in a dangerous practice called "chicken". Euphemistically referred to as a game, it is played by a group of children who stand on the edge of a pavement, preferably at night, and see who can be the last to run across the road in front of an approaching vehicle. Apparently Monkey had only just won the contest when he was hit by a motor-cycle travelling in the opposite direction.

The prognosis was that he would always walk with a limp, which was evident when he was ushered into my study by his splendid little mother. My first impression as he skulked in, head and shoulders thrust forward, was to liken him to Neanderthal Man. Yet the poor lad's shuffling gait was not the reason for his nick-name : that had been bestowed upon him several years earlier and was clearly inspired by his facial features. A clump of unkempt hair was separated from his flat, wide face by a narrow forehead. He had large ears, practically no nose and a very wide mouth full of uneven teeth. To complete his pathetic profile : he was a low achiever of below average intelligence.

His mother's intention was to place the boy into my care with the hope that "Lea Grange could do as well for him as it had done for his brothers, especially Jack". The thought of Jack, who had completed his education with us four years earlier, caused me to wince and to wonder what criteria she employed to evaluate success. I suppose that my achievement in persuading a school governor to employ him as an operative in his slipper works was fairly remarkable, all things considered.

"Why didn't you choose Lea Grange for Alan when he was eleven?"

The diminutive lady seated opposite me nervously shuffled her ankle boots : men's boots, if I'm not mistaken.

"Well, after his dad left, I had a gentleman friend living with us for a while. He chose the other school for Alan. He doesn't live with us anymore."

I played for time: I had to think. "How are Joey and Vince?"

"Vince is doing really well. He finished his joinery training with Ben Lomas last year." This was another

113

placement I'd made. Ben, a member of the Rotary Club, was the local undertaker. He'd accepted my recommendation and Vincent had not let either of us down, as far as I know.

"How about Joey."

"Oh him! He's still living at home, on the dole, a layabout. I don't want Alan to copy him."

I relented. Monkey McNab became a pupil at Lea Grange and made a good initial impression. Paul Robson took him under his wing and gave him extra lessons in English, after school, about three times a week. The boy was a reliable and regular attender, Paul would not have tolerated less, and so his failure to turn up for his reading practice on the day the class-room panel was damaged and on the day following, set Paul's alarm bells ringing.

The facts were that Alan McNab was our only suspect and he was absent from school without explanation. I decided to take the bull by the horns and visit the McNab household without delay.

I arrived just before twelve noon.

"What do you want?" enquired Joey, the nineteen year old layabout.

"I want to see your mother about Alan."

"He's not in. He's where you should be : at school."

Bang, crash, wallop! The teeny-weeny Mrs McNab had sprung into action.

"Don't you dare cheek Mr Firestone," said she, stressing each word with a cuff across Joey's ears, delivered on tip-toe, of course.

"Come in, Sir. Has anything happened to Alan? He went to school this morning."

I entered a most sparsely furnished room bereft of any floor covering except a coat of wood stain on the bare boards. In one corner, facing the obligatory television, were seated a spotty faced youth and two teenage girls, one nursing a baby, undoubtedly Joey's acquaintances. In those days, the only morning programmes were for schools. That day's broadcast was on the Industrial Revolution. They obviously preferred that to gazing at a blank screen.

Before I had completed my explanation of the reason for my visit, Alan could be heard entering the back door. He called from the kitchen.

"What's for dinner Ma?"

"I'll give you dinner. Come in here and tell Mr Firestone where you've been this morning."

Whilst the white-faced lad was still in shock and before he had time to concoct a story, I ascertained that he was responsible for the damage. Joey's friends, to their credit, discreetly departed and the four of us remaining sat down to sort out a solution.

Realising that his brother was in potentially serious trouble Joey did his best to extricate him.

"I'll ask our Vince to help me and we'll repair it. This little bugger, sorry mum, can buy the wood. Let me come back with you and have a look, Mr Firestone."

After considering aloud and at length, whether Alan should be reported to the police for wilful damage, I agreed to defer any action to afford the McNab brothers the opportunity of repairing the panel and restoring the wall to its original state. When Alan dejectedly observed, "Our Vince 'll kill me," I was content to leave punishment to the family's discretion.

Monkey completed his time at Lea Grange unremarkably. Neither he nor the school was able to persuade an employer to engage him. Left to his own devices, he had nothing to commend him and I was not prepared to ruin the chances of future job seekers by falsely giving him our recommendation. Sadly, he began his adult life on the dole.

Cats are said to have nine lives : do monkeys have a similar number of chances? To my knowledge, he had already used up three when I next heard of him almost inevitably from a fellow member of the Rotary Club.

Peter Brown's classification in the Club was "Motor vehicle body repairs". He was an enthusiastic chairman of the "Vocational Service Committee" initiating all kinds of projects to help the local youth to obtain training and, of course, employment. As if that wasn't enough, he ran the church youth club and acted as coach to their football team. He really cared about the welfare of young people : it was fortunate for Monkey that Peter felt as he did.

One day, at the end of the Rotary lunch meeting, he asked me to remain behind. He said that he wanted me to listen to a story about one of my old pupils. He began, "You'll never believe this." I remained silent but feared the worst. He went on, "Last night, young Jimmy (his son) and 'me' went to collect a take-away at Lee Chung's. Whilst we were waiting for our order to be put up, two lads came in. One asked me if I wanted to buy a car radio for six pounds.

'No thanks,' I replied.

'You can have it for five quid.'

'I said no, on your way.'

When I got to work this morning, we'd been broken into."

"And a car radio had been pinched." I was ahead of him.

"That's right. No damage : unscrewed clean as a whistle. It didn't need Sherlock Holmes to put two and two together. I started to 'phone Tom Dyson (another Rotarian, also Police Inspector) but something made me hold back."

"So one of the cars you're repairing is without its radio?"

"Well, no. Instead of ringing the police, I 'phoned home and asked young Jimmy if he knew the lad who tried to sell me the radio. He didn't, but he recognised the other youth. His young brother is in Jimmy's class. I've had a very busy morning, Adam. I went first to the little lad's house and he told me where his big brother's mate lived. So off I went there and got the radio back. The lad who stole it and his mother begged me not to report him to the police. They said you would vouch for him."

"Who is it?"

"Alan McNab."

"Oh no, not him again!"

"Well, can you vouch for him?"

"I don't know about vouching for him. I can certainly give you a fair idea of his back-ground. He hasn't had much going for him so far in life."

"I suspected as much," said my magnanimous friend.

I told Peter all I could remember about Alan McNab : his father's desertion; his ghastly living conditions; the remarkable efforts of his mother despite their penurious situation; and the tremendous handicap of his unlovely appearance, which Peter had already noted.

"Thanks, Adam. You've been fair to the boy."

"What are you going to do?"

"I don't know. I'm going to have a good think."

There was nothing more I could add to what I had told him and Peter did not press me further. We finished our coffee in trite conversation and went our separate ways.

Over the next few weeks I did not hear anything of Alan McNab. At first, I was tempted to ask Peter about the matter but I deemed that no news was good news and I curbed my curiosity. If Peter had decided to settle without involving the police, I didn't want to stir things up.

That's how it was left. Soon, other problems replaced my worries about Monkey McNab and he sank into the deeper recesses of my memory.

I was, therefore, ill prepared for the shock I received almost a year later. On the way home from school, I called at Peter's place of work to deliver a batch of posters my students had prepared to publicise a Rotary dance. As I entered reception I was greeted by a smiling Alan McNab, clad in a white boiler suit.

"Good afternoon, Sir. Can I help you?"

I retained my composure, returned his greeting and listened with interest to how Mr Brown had offered to give him a chance to better himself.

"Is he looking after you all right?" enquired Peter as he came in from the yard. "We are very, very pleased with him."

Five minutes later, in the seclusion of his office, I sat opposite to Peter.

"Why didn't you tell me?" I asked.

"I wanted to see how things turned out. I'm sorry, I should have kept you informed."

"Don't apologise, please. I'm delighted that you've sorted him out. What made you decide to give him a job?"

Peter surprised me with : "Have you read 'Les Miserables' Adam?"

"I know the story," I replied.

"Well, the way the bishop covered up for Jean Valjean and give him the chance to change his life made a big impression on me."

"When he gave him the candlesticks?" I wanted my friend to know that I was au fait with his line of thought.

"Yes, of course," he replied. "When I visited the McNab's and saw the disgusting conditions he was having to grow up in I couldn't help comparing his predicament with the loving care that Jane and I lavish on young Jimmy."

"I know what you mean. Teachers are faced with that kind of dilemma on a daily basis."

"Well, Adam" he continued, "I felt that I could do something really positive to help the poor lad. I think I had been secretly hoping for a chance to reform a down and out. I don't know."

"And Monkey provided you with the opportunity," said I, winding up his story. Then I added, "You're a good man, Peter."

In his usual self-effacing manner, he hid his embarrassment by focusing the spotlight on we. "You're not doing so badly yourself, Adam!"

CHAPTER 14

IT'S A SMALL WORLD

"No man is an Island, entire of it self"

JOHN DONNE 1571-1631

Enter a leading scientist from Poland on a sabbatical in Britain, add a be-spectacled German film director, whose accent unmistakably betrays his origins, and you have the ideal ingredients for a spy story. I'm sure that Buchan or Le Carre would have woven an intriguing tale around such characters. Well, the two fellows really do exist and their involvement with Lea Grange initiated quite a tale of adventure, even if it did fall short of espionage: at least, I believe it did.

Jarek, the Pole, was first to surface. I met him at an international evening organised by the Rotary Club. At this annual event, it was customary to invite twenty foreign nationals through the auspices of the British Council and to allocate each one to a separate Rotarian, who would be responsible for entertaining his particular guest. Of course, the pairings were arranged prior to the function and without the knowledge that Jarek could understand English. So, because his linguistic ability was in doubt I was chosen to host him, on the grounds that, in the two preceding years, I had successfully managed a couple of Russians, both of whom had only a sketchy knowledge of our native tongue.

Vitaly, from Moscow, was, however, fluent in French and he and I found this to be our best means of communication in spite of my limited ability in that language: not that this mattered because I saw very little of him after the formal meal. In fact, he devoted his evening to charming the wives of middle-aged Rotarians with his skills on the dance floor: fox-trots, sambas, quick-steps, tangos, especially tangos. The man danced incessantly, sharing his attention around most generously even to the extent of dancing the last waltz with the President's wife. Dark, suave and wavy haired, the sophisticated Muscovite was a veritable hit with all members of the opposite sex. I am sure that the sequin clad ladies of the Inner Wheel still look back wistfully to that July evening and to the fantasies that Vitaly conjured up for them.

Uri, from Minsk, was a completely different kettle of fish. He dedicated his energies to downing pints of beer as if the end of the world was nigh, all at my expense. A strapping young man, tall and muscular, he had just failed to make the Russian swimming team at the previous Olympics. Uri laughed a lot and he compounded his mirth by regularly slapping me on the back. Undoubtedly, he had a thoroughly enjoyable, if totally inebriated, evening.

The fact that both Uri and Vitaly had clearly enjoyed our hospitality, albeit in different ways, convinced my Rotarian friends that I possessed a unique aptitude for dealing successfully with visitors from behind the Iron Curtain. Accordingly, Jarek was assigned to me and so began a friendship, which was to make quite an impact on my life over the next few years.

Of course, there was nothing spectacular about the way we got to know each other although I do remember liking him from the moment we were introduced. He was one of twenty assorted foreign guests shepherded into the foyer by our splendid contact from the British Council.

The usual and previously successful procedures were adopted: handshakes usually accompanied by kisses on both cheeks and each guest was soon being looked after personally by a designated Rotarian host. Glass in hand, an essential element in the ice-breaking process, they either stood or sat together and the small cocktail bar was soon buzzing with the normal pleasantries associated with forty people all trying to become acquainted at the same time. In the majority of cases language did not present a problem because most educated foreigners, who visit Britain, do speak English. This is particularly the case with visitors from Commonwealth countries, whatever their creed or colour, from the United States and also from some non-English speaking nations, especially Holland. It is sometimes not so plain-sailing with friends from France and Germany and, particularly, Eastern Europe.

Jarek's command of English was better than I expected. This was fortunate because my entire Polish vocabulary was restricted to "Good evening. How are you?" and "Thank you." It would be an exaggeration to describe him as fluent but he had no difficulty in "getting by". Apparently, he was quite skilled in his second language but, as this was Russian, we decided to persevere with English.

Of course, as our conversation developed we did encounter difficulties from time to time and, in such cases, he would re-phrase his statement to make his point. Apart from his relatively narrow vocabulary, which I have already acknowledged as being infinitely superior to my Polish, his main problem was to insert the definite article whether or not it was needed. For instance, I remember him telling me, "I like to go the camping".

However, Jarek had such an engaging personality that none of this mattered. He was powerfully built, of medium height with wide shoulders and he was blessed with a very firm handshake. His hair was fair and wavy and he had blue eyes which gazed steadily from his broad Slavonic face. He had a very well-developed sense of humour and we spent a most enjoyable evening together. This was followed by visits to my home and, by the time he moved on from his work in the north-west, I had learned that he was employed at the Scientific Institute in Warsaw and that he was over in Britain on a one year research programme. He had a wife, whom he loved very much, and two teenage children, a boy and a girl, and he lived on the top floor of an apartment block in Warsaw. About three months after our first meeting Jarek completed his work in Britain and he returned to Poland. I did not hear from him again until the following Christmas Eve.

By then, Gunter, the German film director, had performed his part in the story. His spell at Lea Grange was preceded by a young lady from an English television company who was sent to prepare his ground. The facts were that her organisation was combining with a similar company from West Germany to produce a series of programmes about four typical families of different nationalities: English, German, Polish and Italian. The English family had three sons, all of whom were pupils at Lea Grange. Each programme would have a particular theme and it was on the subject of School that we were to be involved.

The young lady was clearly taken aback by the intensity of questioning to which I subjected her after she had outlined the type of assistance her company was seeking. I do concede that I pressed her for details of all aspects of the proposal before I agreed to allow it to proceed.

My apprehension and suspicions were based upon an experience I had endured with a television company several years earlier. In similar fashion, I had been approached by an attractive young lady who requested our co-operation in a series about the trials and tribulations of a young teacher. For a fairly substantial donation to our school fund, very little would be required in return: some filming of the front entrance with a name board supplied by her company and a few minutes on the school field during one of our lacrosse matches. I readily agreed, supplied her with details of our bank account and, as a matter of interest, asked her to send me a copy of the script.

Several days later I sat in my study fuming at what I had read. The lacrosse game did not present a problem. It was the circumstances surrounding the filming of the front entrance which I could not countenance. Apparently, the main character was a young black teacher who was bringing his school's lacrosse team to play against our school. There was to be an anti-coloured demonstration as he and his team arrived. Banners were to be waved and the school name board, albeit the one supplied by the television company, was to be daubed with the message: "Keep this school white". Although, the name of the school on the board was fictitious, I was sure that local people would recognise our entrance and I was certain that only harm could result from the whole exercise.

Accordingly, I withdrew my permission, to the annoyance of the film-makers, who were unable to persuade another lacrosse playing school to co-operate. Eventually, the series was completed at another school with a soccer match as the focal game.

I am pleased to say that my present visitor was able to allay all my fears and, one day, Gunter appeared. I hope that my facial expression did not convey my surprise when he was shown into my study. He was certainly not what I expected. In fact, the only connection with my idea of a German was his rimless spectacles. In all other respects, he was completely different from my presumptions.

Well over six feet tall, he was slim with long grey hair,. He wore a pair of moccasins with a pale blue denim suit trimmed with lace on the pockets and sleeves. A huge medallion dangled from a gold chain around his neck. I estimated that he was about fifty years of age: in my old-fashioned view, far too mature for the type of spectacle he presented.

He was living proof that first impressions can mislead in that he turned out to be a wonderful person: kind, considerate, caring and most agreeable company. I allocated him a small office base adjacent to mine and, whenever possible, contrived to enjoy breaks and lunchtimes with him. It is significant that these events took place in the early nineteen-seventies because Gunter was clearly affected by the recent history of his fatherland. He was totally against militarism and he was obsessed with the need for nations to live together in peace. I had no difficulty in subscribing to his views and I really enjoyed the two weeks whilst he and his colleagues went about their business.

The British family was last in line to be filmed so Gunter entertained me regularly by relating his experiences in the other three countries. Laughter, pasta and red wine was his favourite description of Italy, a country where he had obviously enjoyed every minute of his stay. Poland had been a pleasant surprise in that the people displayed such warmth and friendship towards him and his crew. His only reservation was that this attitude was more in evidence among the younger generation. He understood that a proportion of those who had lived through the horrors of the Second World War would find it difficult to forget some of the brutal acts of his fellow countrymen, even if they found it in their hearts to forgive. Considering that over five hundred thousand are believed to have perished at the hands of the Nazis, this is understandable.

It was the German family that irritated him the most, mainly by the lengths they were prepared to go to keep up with the Jones's, or should I say, the Schmidts. One instance particularly exasperated him. It concerned the preparations for the filming at their home. Gunter's technical staff had made a preliminary visit to decide where the cameras would be located, basing their decisions on the depth of colour of the furnishings together with the positions of the chairs, tables and cupboards. A strategy was scientifically worked out and the day of the filming dawned.

When the crew returned to the house with Gunter they were devastated to find that the living room was unrecognisable from what they had seen the week before. Everything had been replaced by new purchases: chairs, tables, carpets, curtains and even lampshades were all different and, worse still, in different positions. Gunter was disgusted, attributing it to an inherent inferiority complex which he asserted was characteristic of the German people. I tried to console him by suggesting that an upwardly mobile family in any nation would tend to behave in a similar fashion.

Filming in Lea Grange proceeded without a hitch. Music and sport were prominent and the concluding scenes were of our pupils singing lustily in the morning assembly. Placed behind me, the camera revealed, to all, the wonderful sight of bright, smiling faces, which it was my privilege to enjoy at the start of every school day.

However, there was an amusing spin off from this. When the completed series was to be broadcast, I informed my eighty six year old mother of the details. She had been living in sheltered accommodation for several years and, with understandable maternal pride, she invited her friends and neighbours to join her in the communal hall to view her son's success.

When I saw her a few days later, she said that they had all enjoyed it and she asked me if it would be on television again. I told her that I imagined that it would. "Well then, Adam, next time can you ask them to show it looking at the stage so we can see your face instead of your back!" I was unable to think of a suitable reply.

At Lea Grange, normal service resumed and the memories of Jarek and Gunter were beginning to fade when, on Christmas Eve, a large parcel of presents arrived from Poland. Enclosed was a pressing invitation for my family and me to stay with Jarek and to join him and his family for "the camping" near Krakow.

The dilemma of risking our sons on a trip behind the iron curtain was balanced against the wonderful opportunity of broadening their experience. In fact, there was no contest. Furthermore, the prospect of visiting the school at Lodz, which was featured in the television series, transformed the invitation from tempting to irresistible. So, on a sunny afternoon during the following August, we were enjoying a picnic by the River Cam on our way to Harwich and the ferry. In addition to the normal changes of clothing, we were equipped with a flagon of drinking water, a Calor gas picnic stove , and a large plastic drum filled with mixed green salad. I had studied the A.A. publication, "Motoring in Eastern Europe", and purchased a large scale map-book of our target area.

We arrived in Holland early one Sunday morning and we were soon speeding along the flat, elevated roads. Our intention to buy a bottle of milk from a passing float in the nearest town was quickly abandoned when we realised that no such delivery service existed. We made do with milkless tea and coffee at our first break, which was in a picturesque woodland clearing adjacent to the most hygienic outdoor toilets one could ever imagine.

We soon crossed the border into West Germany and on to its excellent road system which enabled us to reach Helmstedt, on the East German border, by late afternoon. Although we were ahead of schedule, we decided to defer our crossing of the iron curtain until we had refreshed ourselves with an overnight stay. Our chosen abode was a small guest house on the perimeter of the main cobbled square which, in addition to the residences, was surrounded by shops and a cinema. In the early evening, we joined the many local families out for a stroll and we enjoyed four cones of exquisite Italian style ice-cream. My sons were intrigued by a comic book of Laurel and Hardy with their dialogue in German, of course.

The next morning we crossed a few hundred yards of barren land and presented ourselves at the East German check point, where we received very formal treatment from uniformed officials who had forgotten how to smile. As we filled in our details on the official forms, resting the papers on a rough wooden table, I was heartened by the assurance that others had passed that way before us. The proof was scratched on the table's surface: "Kilroy was here!" The obligatory taxes were paid and we were waved on. It was impossible to miss seeing the sentries in their elevated bases resting on high poles, Colditz fashion, peering down at us, sub-machine guns at the ready.

"Stop pointing and look straight ahead," I advised my sons as we moved on to a concrete surfaced autobahn and aimed our bonnet towards Warsaw, a destination which was now prominently displayed on all the major signposts. One noticeable advantage was that fellow motorists were far less aggressive than in the western section of Germany. Speed limits were moderate and were diligently observed. Any inclination to do otherwise was subdued by the presence of the road traffic police, who patrolled in jeeps and waved sub-machine guns in the faces of recalcitrant drivers.

After three hours, we entered Poland where a friendly official joked about our lack of ability to speak his language. We promised to learn enough to address him on our return journey. The indefinable tension which we had sensed in East Germany had disappeared and, with great excitement and expectancy, we motored along the ways used by Napoleon's armies on their way to Russia and, more recently, by Hitler's storm-troopers. I was very pleasantly surprised by the excellent condition of the road surface, due, I suppose to the fact that our route was on the main highway between the Soviet Union and the German Democratic Republic. The plurality of very heavy lorries bore witness to this, making driving difficult at times owing to a combination of the narrowness of the road and my right-hand driving position.

However, we made very good time and this persuaded us to carry on to Warsaw instead of making an overnight stay in Poznan, as planned. My most vivid memory of that journey is the speed at which darkness descended in the mid-continent: one minute it was light, I blinked, and it was dark. I regretted not making the overnight stay as our progress was mainly along country roads blanketed in darkness. It was with great relief that, eventually, we saw the welcoming lights of Warsaw in front of us.

We had arrived one day earlier than planned and my arranged telephone call to Jarek was not answered. It was essential to find shelter for my family and a taxi driver pointed us in the direction of a small hotel two or three blocks away. I had only travelled about fifty yards towards our refuge when, to my horror, the car engine spluttered and we glided to a stop. A few yards away, two couples were engaged in idle conversation under a street lamp. I approached one of the men.

"Do you speak English?"

"No, but he does!"

His companion explained, "Hi! Buddy! I'm Joe from the U.S. of A." and so on. A native of Warsaw, he had settled in America after serving in World War II and he was in Poland on a visit. Fortunately, they were standing outside their home, which was in a large block of flats. The two men pushed my car through a tunnel entrance into a courtyard, assuring me that it would be safe until the suggested time of two o'clock the following afternoon, when they would meet me with a mechanic.

To the strains of "Hello Dolly" blaring out from its dance hall, our new friends directed us to the hotel reception and arranged accommodation for us. Next day, the car problem turned out to be a broken spindle in the petrol pump and, encouraged by the applause of a group of residents, who had crowded around to see the foreigners, the young fat mechanic set up his bench complete with vice, and effected the repair.

Jarek's home was on the top floor of one of the few post-war buildings that remain in Warsaw, the living area being calculated on the number of people in the family. In their case, for Jarek, his wife and two teenage children of different sex, they had a spacious entrance hall, three large rooms, a large kitchen, bathroom, and maid's room. Yes, they had a residential maid.

The rooms were very well appointed and well furnished. One would expect the home a professional family to be tasteful but there was evidence that Czarek's wife had put much thought into making it so comfortable. From this building, which bore such scars of the second world war as bullet and shrapnel holes, they enjoyed panoramic views of a city of modern buildings constructed on the rubble remaining from that conflict. Throughout our stay of eight days we were treated most handsomely: every meal was prepared with great care and every effort was made to give us an interesting and enjoyable holiday. We sampled a number of Polish dishes and most of our language practice was based on meal times. We visited many places of interest, most of which reflected the influence that wars and aggression have had on Polish history. Shrines to groups of people murdered for no apparent reason were to be found at regular intervals on many streets. These memorials were never without freshly cut flowers placed by relatives and friends who had survived those dark days. Perhaps the most startling reminder of Polish suffering was the Gestapo Headquarters building, preserved with all its trappings for posterity to view. The difference in attitudes of young and old Poles to these relics of the past was very marked. Whilst those who remember those terrible times fervently believe that it is the duty of all to honour those who died for Poland, the youth urge that, although war is evil, bygones are bygones and that no useful purpose can be served by constantly looking to the past. Incidentally, it was in considering the youth of Poland that I noted the greatest difference between the two sides of the Iron Curtain. Polish youth appeared to be far more subdued than western youth: perhaps they were in a similar stage of evolution to our youth of the previous generation. I saw no signs of vandalism and the lack of money available to them for spending on enjoyment had one blessing in that there was no market for drug operators. Education was regarded as essential to the further development of the Nation and all children were expected to learn at least one language other than Polish. The fact that Russian was compulsory was generally resented but many children learned English. University students were forced to work for part of their holidays and they did appear to appreciate the education they received.

Through Jarek's connections, I was fortunate enough to spend an afternoon at the Ministry of Education where I discussed common problems of raising the school leaving age. I was reassured to learn that the Poles had similar problems to us with regard to reluctant learners. The Deputy Minister referred to such persons as having been "born on Sunday." He teased me by adding that, from what he had heard, Britain suffered from many born on both Saturday and Sunday. Whilst he was still laughing at his own joke, he readily agreed to my visiting the school at Lodz but he reminded me that it would be closed for the long summer break. Although this was true, all was not lost as Jarek and I discovered when we drove over to Lodz, a couple of days later. In fact, the visit was a dramatic mixture of disappointment, irony and pleasure.

In view of the holiday closure, I did not expect to see the school in operation but I was disappointed to learn from the head caretaker, a mine of information, that I had missed the Headmistress by forty-eight hours. Like his superior at the Ministry, he was highly amused to inform me that, whilst I had driven eastwards to meet her, she had taken a group westwards to a student camp in Italy. I did not find the irony that we could have passed each other on the way to be as funny as he and Jarek seemed to.

Minutes later, my mood had changed as our guide directed us to a display of books and pictures based on the television series. Photographs of Lea Grange and its pupils were actually mounted on the wall of a school in Lodz, Poland. Words cannot describe the pride and pleasure that I experienced and I don't know how long I had been pouring over the material when Jarek suggested that it was time to go.

For me, that visit was the high-light of the trip but only just. The Poles are very aware of their national culture and especially of the achievements of Copernicus and Chopin. We attended two piano recitals, both of which attracted large audiences. One was given in a public park by candlelight. About one thousand people of all ages sat spellbound throughout the performance and I was very much aware of the controlled attitude of the people in such circumstances. We enjoyed strolling in the city on the balmy evenings, visiting the old town and playing football with the local boys, who insisted that their national hero, Lubanski, was equally as good as our Bobby Charlton.

The end of our stay arrived too quickly and it was with sadness that we bade farewell to our hosts, who had escorted us to the outskirts of their city. We soon realised that finding our way home would not be quite as straight-forward as travelling eastwards. There were no signposts labelled, "This way to Britain" whereas, on our outward journey, once we had entered East Germany, all roads seemed to lead to Warsaw.

We were about forty miles from Slubice, which was our intended overnight resting place when our windscreen suddenly shattered and immediately changed into an opaque mass of glass. We had just passed a lorry going in the opposite direction but, fortunately no other traffic was about and so I was able to stop with relative safety.

Whilst I was pondering our predicament, an army vehicle pulled up and its two occupants took charge. They carefully broke away enough glass fragments to provide me with a view of the road ahead, made sure that we were clear about the route to take to Slubice, shook hands, kissed my wife and then sent me on my way with a reassuring pat on the back.

Our rate of progress was severely affected and the possibility that darkness would be upon us before we reached our destination was a real concern. In a small village, I stopped at the general store to buy a bag of sweets and our car was quickly surrounded by would-be helpers. One young man, a student on holiday from Warsaw, spoke reasonable English. He acquired a sheet of cellophane paper and a roll of Sellotape, which enabled us to increase the size of my spy hole and also shield me from the slip-stream and slivers of glass that were continually peeling off the screen.

The young female receptionist at the hotel in Slubice, to whom I had described our predicament, performed a miracle within minutes of our arrival. We had barely reached our allocated room when she telephoned to request my return to reception. There, I met a fellow traveller, a Pole who had settled in England, and who possessed an emergency plastic windscreen, which he readily offered to me. His generosity was in keeping with the warmth and kindness we had received throughout our stay in the country of his birth.

But we still had a long way to go. I have already mentioned that signposting was more complicated on our westward journey and, in fact, we did take a wrong turning in East Germany. When Leipsig became prominent on the signposts, we realised that we had ventured about forty miles out of our way. Although foreigners were forbidden from straying from the autobahns without permission, I decided to cut across country in order to rejoin the correct route somewhere near the Brandenburg Gate. As the roads were deserted, I drove with optimism until we entered a small town square which had three exit roads, all without traffic indications.

To make matters worse, there was an army truck parked a few yards away and its occupants were quickly made aware of our illicit presence by a middle-aged Frau who repeatedly screamed "Autobahn" and pointed to the road along which we had just travelled. I took the bull by the horns and approached the soldiers, with my atlas open at the appropriate page. The officer in charge rejected my pleas, copied his fellow country-woman and dismissed me with the same word "Autobahn". As I dejectedly returned to my car, a tall middle-aged man, dressed in black from his trilby downwards said, "You want Brandenburg?"

In my best German I replied, "Ya". He pointed the way.

"Danke," I called through my window as I sped off down the road he had indicated. The quality of its surface soon deteriorated until at one stage we were driving over red sand. At the only other settlement we encountered, I left the track and drove round the back of the half dozen dwellings rather than stop for the children, whose game of football was blocking the apology for the road. Soon after this, I rejoined the main highway to the west.

In the meantime, official communications must have been very active so that, when I reached the check-point I was directed into a compound and required to surrender my passport. As my only other word of German was, conveniently, "Why?", I repeatedly asked "Varoom?" every time an official appeared.

Finally, a pompous little man in uniform came out of the building, pointed to the plastic windscreen, and enquired,

"Der stein?"

"Ya," I replied.

He reverted to English. "You go now," he said.

Across the frontier, the demeanour of the West German officials was such a contrast. Their friendly waves and shouts of "Hi! How ya doin'?" betrayed the influence of their allies from the U.S.A.

Our crossing back to England was booked via The Hague and, before we embarked, I experienced two contrasting examples of Dutch behaviour. The first was, without doubt, the most frightening incident of the entire expedition. It occurred in a lay-by, which was screened from the main road by a row of bushes. We were just finishing our final picnic before proceeding to the docks when an open top Mercedes pulled up, blocking in our vehicle. The driver, who wore a blazer and white polo neck sweater, spoke. "Hello. You are English, how lovely!" He produced a wrist watch and offered to sell it to me. When I refused he said, "But I want you to have it." As he said this, his two pugilistic-like companions alighted and stood by me, somewhat menacingly. He continued, "I need some money. It is a very valuable watch."

We regarded each other for what seemed an eternity. Then I told him that I had no money as I had paid it all out to get back home after breaking my windscreen. The atmosphere was electric as we stared at each other. Although I was aware that the hench-men were straining to receive orders to man-handle me, I returned his steady gaze without flinching. Suddenly, he barked an order and his two lieutenants vaulted into the rear seat of his limousine and they were gone.

The incident could have left us with a very bad impression of Holland but circumstances quickly intervened to redress the balance. Our propensity for selecting the wrong route led us nearer to Rotterdam than to The Hague and the ferry. As we sat studying our map, a young man tapped on the car window and asked if he could help. Having listened to our predicament, he evaluated our present position in relation to our intended destination, together with the sailing time of the ferry, and decided that there was not a moment to lose.

"Please follow me," he called as he mounted a powerful motor-cycle. In the style of the New York police, we both did a U-turn in the busy road and accelerated in, what I prayed, was now the right direction. In due course, the lone figure ahead of me slowed down and waved us on, pointing to the slip road leading to the ferry. He had redeemed my faith in human nature and I regret that his abrupt farewell left me with no opportunity to express my thanks. The remainder of the homeward journey was uneventful, allowing me the pleasure and delight associated with looking back over two wonderful weeks. And there was an added bonus. I had accumulated enough thematic material to cover my morning assemblies for the whole of the autumn term.

CHAPTER 15

"THE INSPECTION"

"Don't count your chickens before they're hatched."
AESOP

"Don't put on anything special for us. We just want to see the school operating under normal conditions."

"Yes. Right. Actually, the Smoking and Lung Cancer Unit is due to visit us on Tuesday afternoon but I made the booking several months ago. It's connected with a project I've organised for the Fourth Year."

I was talking on the telephone to a voice which had introduced itself as Her Majesty's Inspector Stanley Cunliffe. He was proposing that he and a senior colleague would visit Lea Grange on the following Tuesday to spend the day with us. As it was Thursday afternoon when he called, I felt that he was giving me very little notice. Indeed, both the shortness of the visit and the lack of notice were puzzling.

Normally, an inspection would last for a week and the school would be given at least two months' warning.

"That's fine," he continued. "I'm looking forward to meeting you on Tuesday. We shall arrive in time to attend morning assembly."

"We'll be looking out for you," was all I could muster although I should have liked to ask directly what was the reason for the visitation. Having replaced the telephone in its cradle, I sat staring at my desk diary, now open at the following Tuesday. In spite of what he had said about sticking to our normal routine, I decided to make myself as free as possible on the day. In fact, this caused no difficulty: a few minor adjustments ensured that I could be available to anticipate and forestall any problems that may arise during the visit.

My biggest difficulty was that I had already arranged an appointment for 4.30pm on that Tuesday. I had agreed to meet a local group responsible for organising evening swimming sessions for the handicapped. A number of older pupils had been assisting this worthwhile activity most commendably for almost a year. Suddenly, without warning, all sorts of problems surfaced, ranging from accusations of theft of personal possessions to minor assault. The handicapped blamed some of our pupils who, in turn, accused one of the local organisers of dispensing summary punishment with his fist. It was essential that I attend the meeting yet changing the date was out of the question as, at my request, it had been postponed and rearranged from the previous week.

I decided that my two Deputies would have to rise to the occasion should the inspectors be still around at 4.30. They would engage the local group in polite conversation over a glass of sherry, followed by tea and biscuits, until I appeared.

Satisfied that this was the best solution I could come up with I turned my thoughts to determining the purpose of the inspection. Here was a real challenge to my powers of detection.

Known facts: little notice; short period of visit; very small inspection team.

I had solved the poser within minutes. Obviously they were coming to see me personally about the Circular I had received a month ago: the one from the Minister inviting applications for posts in the inspectorate. Clearly, if it was to be a normal inspection, the staff would have to be given much more notice. The two inspectors were coming to see me and nobody else. I should feel honoured, especially as one was a high-ranker. But I was not sure I wanted to be an inspector. That was irrelevant, I told myself. The point was that those people were coming to observe me in action on my own territory. Whether I liked it or not, a report would be compiled and it would find its way into my file. Acceptance of any offer was secondary to performing well enough to be invited in the first place. Case completed.

The next morning I told the staff what I knew of the proposed visit, which was very little. I stressed that there was no cause for concern: the school was operating at a high level of efficiency and we all had every reason to feel proud.

It might be a good idea to make sure that all exercise books were marked up to date. I quickly added that it was unnecessary for me to make this suggestion to such diligent professionals.

After dismissing morning assembly, I walked over to the piano to where Roger Hansard was placing his music in his stool.

"Although we are not to put anything special on for the inspectors next Tuesday, I think we'll have a pop hymn to finish the assembly," I suggested.

Over the previous two or three months, Roger had been teaching the kids a few modern versions of hymn tunes. There was a wonderful tradition of music in the area and the children upheld the high standards set by their parents. The singing in our school assemblies was nothing short of beautiful.

Roger suggested the most recent offering: a modern version of 'All Creatures of our God and King'.

"If you don't mind, Roger, I want us to be spot on. I'd like you to play your Dixieland version of 'Onward Christian Soldiers'. Ask Stephen to bring his banjo and I'll make up on the drums."

"Yes, that's perhaps a better idea. 'Onward Christian Soldiers' never fails," he agreed.

From then on I decided to mention the visit as little as possible because, if I appeared anxious, the staff would be affected likewise. However, as Friday progressed, I became aware of all kinds of deficiencies that would be glaringly obvious to the inspectors. Furthermore, I found myself becoming increasingly enthusiastic about joining Her Majesty's Inspectorate and I was determined that my chances should not be spoilt by some difficulty that could be foreseen and prevented. The litter in the corner of the school field by the tennis courts, blown by prevailing south-westerlies and periodically cleared by our pupils as an alternative to physical education, was more of an eyesore than I could remember. The small brass shields on the House Trophy Boards had not been cleaned for weeks and the broken chairs, stored in the cloakroom, awaiting repair, must be hidden somewhere.

Fortunately, the Art Department had just mounted a display on the walls of the assembly hall. This, together with the photographs and drawings of a recent geographical field trip displayed in the entrance hall, were as much as I could wish for, given the amount of time at my disposal.

Day minus one dawned. At the morning assembly on that Monday, all that remained was to prepare the kids for the visit. I confined the information to a brief reference that we were to welcome two visitors on the following day and that if, in the morning, any of them saw a couple of strangers apparently looking for my study they were to greet them politely and bring them along.

Although I was not eagerly looking forward to the visit, I felt satisfied that there was nothing else I could do to prepare for this important milestone in my career. The litter had been cleared from the tennis courts and, over the weekend, the broken chairs had been spirited away. The House Shields were gleaming.

I must thank Bill Brown, our caretaker. Indeed, henceforth I resolved to refer to him by his preferred title, school-keeper, instead of giving him the less exalted title of caretaker. As he had recently grown a moustache and taken to wearing a tie, it was the least I could do. Like all caretakers, he thought of and, indeed, referred to the building as 'his school'. His extremely high standard of work deserved some reward and I never dreamed of depriving him of the pleasure he derived from this delusion of ownership.

On Tuesday morning I made a very early start. I needed to clear the post and then to settle down and look comfortably in charge. I drew some comfort from one circular extolling the virtues of an anti-graffiti liquid. The leaflet bore a photograph of a Northampton Headteacher who swore by the liquid, having used it successfully for several years. What an idiot, I thought, to admit that graffiti appears in one's school, let alone circulate the information to all the schools in Britain, accompanied by one's picture. I felt that my procedure of training my caretaker, sorry, school-keeper, to immediately remove any suggestions of graffiti, was far more effective. I destroyed the circular lest the inspectors may see it lying about and assume that we had problems requiring the aid of such commercial preparations.

Much to my relief, it was a beautiful, sunny day. There would be none of the dinner-time problems that rainy days bring: especially the almost impossible task of trying to supervise a multitude of exuberant kiddies in a building that was too small and of inadequate design. Thank goodness Jean Lennox was down to do dinner duty. In all my years of teaching I have never known anyone with such quiet control. Hardly ever resorting to unpleasantness and never raising her voice, she always presided over orderly, purposeful groups: formal lessons; sports practices; yard duty; the dining hall. I have never worked out the reason for her success. She was good looking, possessed shapely legs and drove a two-seated open sports car. Inherent confidence and determination were probably nearer the mark.

My first visitor arrived earlier than expected, ushered in by a first-year boy beaming with triumph., Hardly had we shaken hands when Senior Inspector Bowden burst in, grinning broadly.

"I've just been welcomed by an angel!"

Behind him, smiling demurely, stood Glenys Stacey, one of our loveliest girls. I could not have contrived a better beginning. I must not let the importance of the occasion spoil my performance. I really wanted to impress my two guests who, incidentally, could not have been more different. The younger Cunliffe, dark grey suit and rimless spectacles, was formal, serious and utterly correct. If anything, I felt he was a little too deferential to Bowden whose casual air and dress surprised me. A brown harris tweed jacket with baggy grey slacks and a woolly checked shirt seemed out of place for a senior representative of Her Majesty charged with the task of assessing me.

Cunliffe immediately launched into serious questions about the catchment area, the socio-economic make-up of the school roll and such like whilst Bowden joked about the problems a Yorkshire man must be encountering as a Headmaster in Lancashire.

The bell for assembly came as a relief. My guests declined my invitation to join me on the platform. They preferred to view the proceedings from the rear. I remember nothing about the ceremony until the final hymn, which was a resounding success. Hearty singing was backed by my two instrumentalists, who really excelled themselves. The banjo must have been invented to accompany "Onward Christian Solders"! As verse followed verse, the enjoyment gathered momentum. Suddenly, old Bowden stood, raised his index finger and began to shake in the best jitterbug tradition, finally resuming his seat and mopping his brow as the last verse ended. As I stepped forward to issue the daily notices, he began to clap, nudging Cunliffe who joined in the applause.

My highest hopes were already exceeded. After such a fantastic beginning it would have been difficult for the day to be anything but successful.

Having freed myself from all routine commitments, I had hoped to spend the morning shepherding my guests into the rooms of my choosing: the rooms where I could guarantee that purposeful work would be evident. My best made plans were ruined when my two visitors decided to split up and move off in opposite directions. Whom should I accompany? I held my nerve and smiled bravely. I watched them go.

"I'll be around, if you need me." A more original comment deserted me. I need not have worried. By the time we re-grouped and took our lunch with the pupils, a most civilised experience, my two guests could hardly conceal their enjoyment and approval.

Duly refreshed, we enthusiastically moved on to the afternoon project, the pre-arranged presentation on smoking and lung cancer. I had organised the discussion groups to accommodate the two chaps whom I was beginning to regard as future colleagues. The project was introduced by two extremely attractive females, both in their mid-twenties, I guessed. Apart from the fact that our senior guest paid far too much attention to the smaller of the two, a red-head with a most engaging smile, the afternoon passed without incident. At 3.45pm, Cunliffe and I sat in my study awaiting Mr Bowden for a final meeting. Eventually, he joined us. Rather flushed but obviously pleased with himself, he explained that he had been thanking the two 'gels' for their wonderful exhibition. As I had gone to great lengths to express our appreciation to them in the formal setting, supported by loud and sustained applause from the pupils, I could not help feeling that he was overdoing the charm.

Comfortably seated with tea in china cups:

"No milk, thanks, just a little sugar", they exchanged glances. Almost imperceptibly, Bowden lowered his head about one centimetre in what I could only assume was a nod and Cunliffe wriggled forward so that he was sitting on the edge of his seat. He raised his right hand with his thumb and index finger forming a ring. Smiling he said,

"Mr Firestone, you've got a jewel in your school. Personal relationships are superb: the kids; the teachers; the ancillaries. It's an intangible phenomenon but it's all permeating. Is that not so Sir?"

"Most definitely, I have not enjoyed myself as much for years. It's wonderful for an office bound chap like me to see what excellent work goes on in our schools." Bowden added.

There followed from Cuncliffe a predictable summing up of his impressions and suddenly they both rose, shook hands with me, and left. I expected someone to say something like you'll hear from us or we'll let you know.

Apart from, "Thanks again for a lovely day", there was nothing.

I had twenty minutes to spare before my 4.30 meeting about which I recall very little. I remember everyone leaving in a happy frame of mind after about two hours.

The next morning I was still wondering how and when they would let me know if I was to be recommended for Her Majesty's Inspectorate. At about 10am there was light knock on my door. It opened slightly and Cunliffe's bespectacled head enquired, "Are you busy? May I come in?"

"Please. Please have a seat."

"Do you think we can have a large jug of coffee? I want to talk to you."

"Certainly." I leapt from my chair and ordered coffee with chocolate biscuits.

Ten long minutes later, separated by a tray of coffee and biscuits, with my door firmly closed and bearing my hardly-ever used 'Do Not Disturb' sign, Cunliffe looked over his glasses and asked,

"You know what yesterday was all about?"

Not wishing to appear presumptuous and, in any case, wanting to hear my good news from him, I feigned puzzlement by a shrug and a grimace. He continued, "I'm absolutely delighted. I didn't dream it would be so easy. Bowden is such an awkward cuss. You and your school were so helpful. You see, yesterday was a mock inspection to mark the end of my two years' probationary period. I am now a fully fledged H.M.I. I only picked your school with a pin, what an excellent choice I made!"

I trust that my facial expression did not betray my feelings: surprise, astonishment and a slight bruising of the ego. It was a simple and logical reason for the visitation that my inflated self-importance had not even considered.

Fortunately, Cunliffe was so euphoric about his own success that any blinks or grimaces from me would be unnoticed. In any case, I quickly recovered my composure and it was then that I resolved to banish from my mind all delusions of grandeur and to devote the remaining fifteen years of my working life to the job I did best.